IDEAS &
INSPIRATIONS

from
HOMES
& GARDENS
MAGAZINE

IDEAS &
INSPIRATIONS

from
HOMES
& GARDENS
MAGAZINE

© IPC Magazines Limited 1995

Text © Annuals Publishing Limited 1995
Illustrations © Suppliers as featured, unless otherwise marked; selected illustrations © IPC Magazines Ltd

Published by Annuals Publishing Limited
1 High Street, Princes Risborough, Buckinghamshire HP27 0AG
under licence from IPC Magazines Limited

This book was compiled, edited and designed for the publishers by
Duncan Petersen Publishing Ltd

Editor	Leonie Glass
Assistant Editor	Catherine Palmer
Written by	Leonie Glass and Laura Harper
Researched by	Catherine Palmer, Laura Harper, Judy McMillan, Lucy Hutchinson and Andrew Duncan
Original concept	Fiona Duncan
Acknowledgements	The editor would like to thank the following people at Homes & Gardens for their help: Blossom Martis, Joanna Laidlaw, Pippa Rimmer, Tracey Corfield and Atlanta Bartlett; also Julia Pieri at Robert Harding Picture Library, and Peta Levi at New Designers in Business.
Art Director	Mel Petersen
Designers	Chris Foley and Beverley Stewart

Typeset by Duncan Petersen Publishing Ltd
Originated by Reprocolor International SRI, Milan
Printed and bound by New Interlitho Italia S.p.a, Milan

ISBN 1 899107 04 5

ABOUT THIS BOOK

Many of the people featured in this book make a variety of products. A number appear in different sections and a cross-reference in **bold** will direct you to the other entry or entries. The text indicates the range produced by each individual or company but, with space at a premium, there hasn't always been room for all the details. Many craftsmen will undertake specific commissions and welcome individual enquiries.

On pages 185-7, there is a list of the contributors to this book, organized by region, so that, if for example you're on holiday in Devon, you can visit a potter who has a local workshop, or in Scotland, a small textile manufacturer. Please remember that it is always advisable to telephone for an appointment first. Where a visit is inappropriate, a mail-order catalogue is usually available.

Where possible, prices have been given. Sometimes this has not been possible – usually because the item needs to be specially commissioned. In these cases there is a phone number which you can call in order to discuss prices. Unless specified, prices include VAT. Where numerous items are illustrated, a price range has been included.

A pleasant way to see and purchase the work of some of the contributors is at the various exhibitions and craft shows that are held throughout the year. Dates change annually, but the following list gives the usual month of the exhibition and a number to telephone for further information.

Feb	*Daily Telegraph Period Homes & Gardens Show*	0171-436 1515
Feb-Mar	*Country Living Fair*	0171-439 5296
Mar-Apr	*Daily Mail Ideal Home Exhibition*	01895-677677
Apr-May	*Top Drawer (trade only)*	0171-370 8185
May	*Chelsea Flower Show*	0171-834 4333
June	*Homes & Gardens Summer Grand Sale**	(Information available through *Homes & Gardens* magazine).
Sept	*Top Drawer (trade only)*	0171-370 8185
Sept-Oct	*Decorex (trade only)*	0171-833 3373
Oct	*Chelsea Crafts Fair*	0171-278 7700
Nov	*At home - The Design for Living Event*	(Information available through *Homes & Gardens, Country Homes and Interiors, Ideal Home* and *Homes & Ideas* magazines)
Nov	*Homes & Gardens Christmas Grand Sale**	(Information available through *Homes & Gardens* magazine)

Throughout the year, exhibitions are staged at the *Crafts Council Gallery*, Pentonville Rd, London N1 9BY. Tel.: 0171-278 7700.

* To exhibit at the Homes & Garden Grand Sales, contact The Value for Money Company (tel.: 0171-351 3088).

CONTENTS

CONTENTS

INTRODUCTION

*by Amanda Evans,
Editor of
Homes & Gardens magazine*

Anyone who loves their home relishes the discovery of a decorating accessory that is unique or unusual. People will travel miles because they've heard of a village blacksmith who has started forging door hinges or of a warehouse full of antique bedheads. Indeed, because of the hard research work involved in seeking out these one-off shops or craftsmen and women, most people guard their names jealously. If they tell you at all, they'll implore you to keep it a secret. Now, thanks to *Ideas & Inspirations* from *Homes & Gardens* magazine, all that foot slogging is over.

As a magazine *Homes & Gardens* is dedicated to giving its readers the very best information on homes, decorating, gardens and the latest accessories. Indeed, our many pages of interesting and unusual merchandise each month have been gathered thanks to the tireless research of our various decorating and features editors. It has taken years to build up such a varied range of names and addresses – and we think that it's time you got your hands on this valuable list.

So, for the first time ever, we have gathered these exciting names together and put them into one book – a book packed with the names and addresses of designers of one-off objects, craftsmen and small retailers – and, of course – photographs to represent their work. We've tried to get as many names into the book as possible, but it is almost inevitable that there will be some omissions and for this I apologise. We

hope to make good any faults in future editions.

I hope you enjoy *Ideas & Inspirations*. It is designed with ease of reference in mind, indexed under category and by name. Fun to read at any time, it will be essential when you need to start looking for the finishing touches. In fact, we hope that it will prove to be as important an object around your house as the plug sockets in the walls or the handles on the doors: the key to making your home *yours* – through countless individual touches.

Tables & Chairs

Dramatic contemporary dining furniture... elegant classic designs hand-crafted in polished wood or wrought iron... innovative occasional tables... formal high-backed thrones... and chairs to relax in.

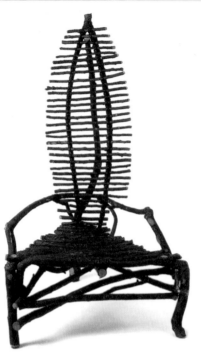

▽ 'Trilogy' is a three-sided desk in cherry, bog-oak and patinated bronze, with separate working areas and cantilevered drawers, made in the John Makepeace Studio (see also p. 14, and **Cupboards and Chests**). A highly skilled team designs and makes imaginative and inventive objects. The price for a large specially designed piece, such as this, ranges between £15,000 and £30,000. *John Makepeace Studio, Parnham House, Beaminster, Dorset DT8 3NA. Tel.: 01308-862204.*

◁ As their name suggests, Sparewood manufacture furniture from 'found' wood: driftwood, orchard cuttings, disused farm ladders and posts, and so on. This unusual chair, which would be equally at home inside or outside, is made from applewood cuttings and costs about £130, from *Sparewood, Cambridge Cottage, Cambridge Lane, Lynsted, Kent ME9 9JB. Tel.: 01795-521392.*

▷ MDW Design make minimalist, graceful furniture and accessories in aluminium and pewter, with a smooth finish. The price for this chair starts at £150, depending on the fabric used; the dining-table costs £1,965. Their wide-ranging accessories are tactile yet sturdy and practical, and include corkscrews, candleholders and mirrors. Furniture can be made to commission, in aluminium, wood or plastic, from *MDW Design, Studio 13, Giffin Business Centre, Giffin St, London SE8 4RJ. Tel.: 0181-691 0605.*

△ Made from beautifully figured solid satinwood with walnut inlay, this dressing-table was specially commissioned. It contains an unusual central well with covering lids that slide away to each side. Simon Clark works alone, both designing and making furniture to commission. Prices start at about £1,500 for a small occasional table in well-figured hardwood with detail. *Simon Clark Cabinetmaking, Rodgrove Farm, Wincanton, Somerset BA9 9QU. Tel.: 01963-370261.*

▽ Andrew Varah made these chairs in ash and blue aspen to achieve maximum comfort and an air of lightness, with the minimum of material. The curved arm and seat are laminated in solid birch. Andrew and his team of five young craftsmen design and make one-off items of modern furniture, mainly for private homes, with prices ranging from £200 to £20,000. Andrew established his workshop more than 20 years ago, and specializes in complicated commissions, many of which include a secret compartment to defeat any burglar. His designs are extremely versatile. Contact *Andrew Varah, Little Walton, Near Pailton, Rugby, Warwickshire CV23 0QL. Tel.: 01788-833000.*

▷ Dramatically different, this oak throne by Jim Crockatt contains copper and ebony inlay and stands 1.5m high. Jim undertakes wide-ranging commissions, and in the last eight years he has developed his own 'organic' style of furniture, using natural shapes sympathetic to the grain, pattern and texture of the wood (see also **Cupboards and Chests** and **Crafts for Children**). Contact *Jim Crockatt, Pococks Cottage, Mariners Lane, Bradfield, Berks. RG7 6HX. Tel.: 01734-744728.*

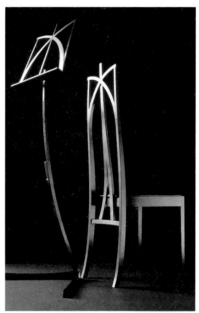

▷ This unique ebony chair echoes the graceful design of the music stand it accompanies and is made by Neil Wyn Jones at Artizana (see also **Small Furniture**), a showcase for the work of over 70 British furniture-makers, as well as decorative artists and craftsmen. This chair was made for £520. Artizana accept commissions for sculpture, jewellery, silver, ceramics, textiles and glass to produce one-off contemporary pieces (see also **Silver**). *Artizana, The Village, Prestbury, Cheshire SK10 4DG. Tel.: 01625-827582.*

△ This Book Table is made from MDF, with a lift-up lid and plenty of space inside. A handy storage place, it also functions as an occasional table. CVP Designs supply it either hand-painted with *faux* books in a choice of colours (for £865), or in white eggshell (£450), for you to choose your own titles (they recommend that a professional painter completes the job). Also available is a small range of decorative accessories, from *CVP Designs, 27 Bruton Place, London W1X 7AB. Tel.: 0171-491 3724.*

◁ Taken from the Creation Collection by John Makepeace (see also p. 12 and **Cupboards and Chests**), Vine was carved by hand in limewood and hand-coloured, making an excellent example of the collectable furniture produced to commission by the John Makepeace Studio. A similar piece could be made for approximately £12,000. For more information, contact *John Makepeace Studio, Parnham House, Beaminster, Dorset DT8 3NA. Tel.: 01308-862204.*

◁ Echoing the Regency period, this detailed writing desk is handmade in walnut, using traditional techniques. It measures 80cm high x 105cm wide and 48cm deep, and in walnut costs £1,786. Trevor Moore's extensive range, designed and made by hand, includes sewing tables, washstands, a box seat and blanket chest, and an unusual kitchen. Much of his work is available hand-painted or natural, in a variety of woods, and can be seen at his Devizes showroom. *Trevor Moore Handmade Furniture Ltd, The Wharf Centre, Couch Lane, Devizes, Wilts. SN10 1EB. Tel.: 01380-727441.*

▽ Each piece in the Radnor Collection has an air of strength and solidity, and signals fluency. An architectural and interior designer, Philip Hearsey produces a broad range of bespoke furniture and fittings for individual projects. He collaborates with highly talented craftsmen to make one-off pieces or limited series. The skill of the blacksmith is evident; the elegance of hand-forged steel is used to great effect when combined with the organic strength of hunks of British hardwoods, or contrasted against crisp glass or polished stone. Prices start at £150, from *Philip Hearsey, Monkhall Court, Callow, Hereford HR2 8DA. Tel.: 01432-351170.*

▷ Italian and Rococo influences are evident in such timeless pieces as this armchair, supplied for £420.65 with natural canvas cushions, or more with the fabric shown. The Iron Design Company hand-craft their classic metal furniture for both interior and exterior settings. They boast a wide choice of tables and chairs, as well as bedheads, screens and kitchen storage racks. They also make furniture to customers' specifications. Contact *The Iron Design Company, Summer Carr Farm, Thornton-Le-Moor, Northallerton, N. Yorks. DL6 3SG. Tel.: 01609-778143.*

▽ Striving to maintain the integrity of traditional ironwork design, Paul Shepherd produces furniture such as this table with elm top and delicate detail, which costs £420. His work includes large gates, railings and panels; also tables, mirrors, bowls and candle-holders. He welcomes commissions. Contact *Paul Shepherd, Lower Nicholson, Docklow, Leominster, Hereford HR6 0SL. Tel.: 01568-760430.*

△ Tom Faulkner combines elegant wrought-iron with either distinctive hand-painted table-tops or glass, as shown here, to make tables and chairs to order. Bold flowing curves and classical simplicity characterize his designs, from dining-tables to bedside tables, equally at ease in traditional or the most modern of settings. This coffee table measures 1m sq. and costs £399, from *Tom Faulkner Designs, 13 Petley Rd, London W6 9SU. Tel.: 0171-610 0615.*

◁ Ancient jarrah wood, originally cut in Australia in 1880 and turned into sleepers for the South African railways, has been recycled to make truly original pieces designed by Hormoz Karim. African craftsmen sculpt this extraordinary wood into a variety of tables, chairs – such as this one-off carver – beds, stools and so on. The timber is hard as stone, virtually indestructible, and extremely resistant, polishing up beautifully. Prices start at £300. *The Hill Gallery, 39-51 Highgate Rd, London NW5 1RS. Tel.: 0171-267 0457.*

△ Ideal for bookworms, this Library Chair is manufactured in softwood, which is painted and waxed, and houses a substantial number of books on its fitted shelves, on each side. The chair also incorporates a drawer under the seat and is made to order (oak also available) in a range of colours and sizes, starting at £450. Zwerlin accept commissions for other free-standing furniture including tables, chairs, dressers and dining-tables, in a variety of materials. *Zwerlin, The Sub-Basement, Trowbray House, 108 Weston St, London SE1 8QB. Tel.: 0956-416623.*

▽ The ingenious construction of 'La Dolce' folding rocking chair makes it less than 5kg in weight, and allows it to be flipped open speedily. Designed ergonomically for superb comfort, it adjusts for sitting upright or lounging. Constructed in ecologically sound European hardwood, it features solid brass fittings and removable slips, and is suitable for indoors and out. When folded, it measures 107.5 x 57.5 x 15cm. The canvas comes in cream, black or various colours. Leather is an alternative. The chair costs £219, including VAT, + p & p. This designer makes furniture to commission, also acts as a consultant, and produces a limited range. Order direct from *Richard Joseph Ward, 7b Ezra St, London E2 7RH. Tel.: 0171-729 6768.*

◁ Recollections Furniture Company makes an extensive range of exact copies of Shaker furniture, such as this simple rocking chair. Every item is entirely handmade. This chair is constructed in English cherry, but can be made in any wood, and at the same price. The seat is fashioned from handwoven Herefordshire rushes, and the chair measures 145 x 89 x 53.2cm. It costs £665, from *Recollections Furniture Company, Whitehill Park, Weobley, Hereford HR4 8QE. Tel.: 01544-318092.*

▽ The Heveningham Collection by Annie Eadie is a range of elegant wrought-iron furniture for both interior and exterior use, handcrafted in the UK. Based on old Italian designs, and ranging from luxury chaise longues, dining-tables and chairs to Versailles tubs, this collection suits a variety of locations, from dining-rooms and conservatories to terraces and pool surrounds. High-quality materials are used, with emphasis on preparing the metal thoroughly before applying weather-resistant paint. Prices start at £135, from *The Heveningham Collection, Peacock Cottage, Church Hill, Nether Wallop, Hants. SO20 8EY. Tel.: 01264-781124.*

TABLES AND CHAIRS

▷ Made from maple, this occasional table by Stemmer & Sharp measures 66cm high x 48cm wide and costs £275 (also available in cherry). Andrea Stemmer and Fiona Sharp design and make functional and innovative contemporary furniture in wood, inspired by the sparseness and clarity of Japanese design. They work for production and to commission, liasing closely with a client. Sustainable hardwoods only are used. *Stemmer & Sharp, 2 Wren St, London WC1X 0HA. Tel.: 0171-837 1627.*

▽ 'L'Occhio' – a polished wrought-iron chair – is designed by Claire Nelson, and costs £240, plus 1.5m of fabric. Nelson Design can make furniture to any specification, offering both contemporary and traditional styles. Highly versatile, they will, for example, advise and make up a window treatment; plan and design a new kitchen or bathroom; or refurbish an entire house; as well as furnish restaurants, shops and offices. *Nelson Design, 169 St. John's Hill, London SW11 1TQ. Tel.: 0171-924 4542.*

△ Bill Gill uses a computer to help design his futuristic furniture, and to laser-cut sheets of mild steel to make his bold, invigorating designs. To this stool, he has added a silver epoxy finish and rubber-disk shock absorbers. It can be packed flat. It measures 42.5cm high and costs £135. Bill also makes tables, mirrors and shelving, which either flat-pack or dismantle. Contact *Bill Gill, 13 Riverbank, East Molesey, Surrey KT8 9BH. Tel.: 0181-979 2871.*

◁ John Lowday painstakingly follows ancient Celtic designs to make his sugán (Irish rope) chairs in native oak or ash. The chairs are extremely strong and pleasing to the eye, and come in six comfortable designs, plus chairs for children. John also produces various tables and a Celtic kitchen dresser. All his furniture is finished in teak oil. The chairs are sold from stock or made to order. The price range is £450–650 for a set of four. *John Lowday, Exeham Farm, Exebridge, Dulverton, Somerset TA22 9AY. Tel.: 01398-323776.*

◁ Glenn Hinton creates unusual furniture, employing hand-carving techniques. He combines indigenous woods, stone, glass and metal with sensitivity and attention to detail. This 'Eye' dining-chair is hand-carved in scorched English oak, with copper inlay and a leather seat. As a one-off it costs £1,200; for a set of eight, each chair costs £800, from *Glenn Hinton Furniture, Croft Rd, Sudbury, Suffolk CO10 6RD. Tel.: 01787-376787.*

▽ Antiques from the 18th and 19thC have inspired the designs found in the Monica Pitman Collection (see also **Decorative Accessories** and **Lighting**). Metal furniture, lighting and decorative objects are hand-finished to high standards, using modern materials, yet retaining the character of the original pieces. Special colours and sizes are available to order for contract use. This round, rope-and-tassel dining-table measures 72cm high x 102cm in diameter, also comes in a rectangular shape, and costs £733. The collection includes a variety of metal tables and chairs, étagères and large, ornamental lemon and orange trees in painted metal. *The Monica Pitman Collection, M5 Chelsea Garden Market, Chelsea Harbour, London SW10 0XE. Tel.: 0171-376 3180.*

▷ The Square-Bar range by A'Fos includes dining-tables and chairs, tall lamp tables and coffee tables. Durable in solid mild steel, these pieces come with a choice of table-tops – slate, hardwood and MDF – and three finishes. This chair costs £159, minus the fabric cover. A'Fos is a design business and a shop, selling furniture, lighting, accessories and gifts in high-quality modern design, from *A'Fos, Lake Rd, Bowness-on-Windermere, Cumbria LA23 2JJ. Tel.: 015394-47766.*

▽ Each piece in the Contemporary Classics range is made to order, available in a wide choice of materials and details. This 'Cotmore' dining-table costs about £1,000. Lucinda Leech has been making furniture for more than 15 years. She and her team work to a wide range of commissions, with a fine eye for detail, in any timber, employing 100% sustainable material, and liaising closely with a client. Contact *Lucinda Leech Furniture, King St, Jericho, Oxford OX2 6DF. Tel.: 01865-56376.*

△ This Roman Mosaic coffee table incorporates small tesserae pieces set in a metal base. It measures 147.5 x 85cm, and costs £875. Alex Shaftel embellishes old furniture with an array of cracked ceramic tiles from all over the world, and designs pieces from scratch, creating a traditional-looking 'Roman' mosaic to contemporary effect. New designs include tables, frames, mirrors, cabinets and shelves, from *Alex Shaftel Designs, 15-17 Clapham Common Northside, London SW4 0RG. Tel.: 0171-720 6822.*

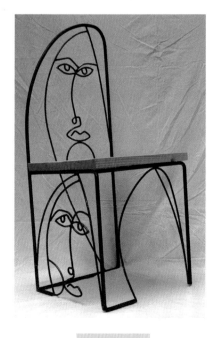

◁ The Alice Chair is just part of this designer's range of individually created works: hand-painted screens, silvered mirrors in unique frames, a variety of tables, metal chairs for inside and out, and hand-decorated papier mâché bowls, using gesso to create a porcelain-like finish. This chair comes plain or painted, with a wooden or upholstered seat; sold on its own or in pairs. Upholstered, it costs £190, from *Alice Leach, 57 Pennard Rd, London W12 8DW. Tel.: 0181-746 0387.*

◁ 'Mainstream II', a glass-topped dining-table in American cherry to seat eight, is derived from studies of moving water. It costs £2,800. Ben Brooks concentrates on sparseness of line and simplicity of form, while relying on traditional cabinet-making techniques. He sells internationally, producing functional and intriguing one-off pieces to any budget, for both corporate and private commissions. Contact *Ben Brooks, 1-4 Prince of Wales Terr., London W4 2EY. Tel.: 0181-742 7520.*

▽ This stylish glass-topped dining-table is by Mark Francis, who has been designing and making wrought-iron furniture for the past 12 years. The 'Petworth' range includes a variety of tables and upholstered chairs. Incorporating modern and traditional features, his designs blend with any environment, indoor or out. Prices range from £300 to £700. Mark also welcomes commissions. Contact him or visit his showroom at *New Street House, New St, Petworth, W. Sussex GU28 0AS. Tel.: 01798-343943.* See also **The Garden**.

◁ Inspired by the dynamic geometry of spiral shells, this 'Nautilus' occasional table was designed and made to order by Robin Thomson for £470. The base and shelves are crafted in birch and maple, finished in an almond-white lacquer; the toughened glass top is 10mm thick and cushioned by buffers.
A broad range of designs for commissioned free-standing and fitted furniture is offered by *Robin Thomson, Unit Five, Pottery Lane, Warham St, Kennington, London SE5 0SX. Tel.: 0171-735 7043.*

▽ Lee Sinclair and his highly skilled team make the 'Convertable'. An inspired design allows a small coffee table to convert smoothly to a large, low occasional table, a games table, a dining-table for up to six, and an angled drawing board. Made from ash, antique pine or cherry, with a choice of finish, it starts at £375. Lee also designs and makes modern, classic furniture on commission. Contact *Lee Sinclair Furniture, Endon House, Laneham, Nr Retford, Notts. DN22 0NA. Tel.: 01777-228303.*

◁ Niggy Thomas (see also **Cupboards and Chests** and **Paint Effects**) transformed this ordinary kitchen chair with his mastery of detailed painting techniques. He works to commission, and will apply his skill to walls, floors and furniture. Prices depend on the complexity of the work. For more information, contact *Niggy Thomas, 18 Ashmount Rd, London N19 3BJ, Tel.: 0171-272 6078* or *01625-525205.*

▽ This large, solid table in ash with Indian rosewood detail is made by Brendan Devitt-Spooner. It costs £1,600 and is available in a choice of woods. Employing the finest natural hardwoods and selected tropical woods, Brendan specializes in commissions to make tables, chairs, dressers, desks, cabinets and complete room sets in contemporary styles. Contact *Brendan J. Devitt-Spooner, Wood Design Workshops, The Acre, Dappers Lane, Angmering, W. Sussex BN16 4EN. Tel.: 01903-776010.*

Alouette Innovation Ltd, *PO Box 2264, Epping, Essex CM16 4AH (Tel.: 01992-561265)*, are designers, manufacturers and distributors of high quality multi-level furniture in woods such as American cherry.

Cato Furniture Makers, *The Epstein Building, Cato St, Bristol BS5 6JL (Tel.: 0117-935 4774)*, design and make individual pieces to commission including a figured French pearwood dining-table and chairs.

Robin Clarke Furniture, *Keeper's House, Brockmanton, Pudleston, Nr Leominster, Hereford HR6 0QU (Tel.: 01568-760272)*, handmake traditional country chairs in elm, ash and oak.

Illingworth and Partridge, *160 North St, Milborne Port, Sherborné, Dorset DT9 5EW (Tel.: 01963-251102)*, use fine timber from Europe and North America to produce sensitively designed furniture.

i tre, *Chilcombe, Nr Bridport, Dorset DT6 4PN (Tel.: 01308-482666)*, run by Petter Southall, specializes in limited editions in English hardwoods.

Cleo Muffi *(Tel.: 0171-498 2727)* makes striking mosaic tables as well as wall panels, plates, tiles and garden pots.

David Savage, *Westcombe Lane, Bideford, Devon EX39 3JQ (Tel.: 01237-479202)*, produces original designs for tables and chairs in a variety of hardwoods.

The Somerset Willow Co., *The Wireworks Estate, Bristol Rd, Bridgwater, Somerset TA6 4AP (Tel.: 01278-424003)*, make furniture from woven Somerset willow, ranging from tables, chairs and sofas to toy, laundry and dog baskets.

Trannon Furniture Ltd, *Chilhampton Farm, Wilton, Salisbury, Wilts. SP2 0AB (Tel.: 01722-744577)*, are specialists in designing and batch-producing steam-bent furniture.

Cupboards & Chests

Tall or short, large or small, natural wood or hand-painted, doors or drawers... cupboards, chests, cabinets and wardrobes, handmade by contempory craftsmen.

▽ Adding an air of Arabian splendour, the Tented Wardrobe by Hoppé Design (see also **Beds**) can be fitted with standard shelves, if necessary. It is supplied in kit form for £75, for you to make up in a choice of fabric. At an extra cost, it comes in natural calico with a striped ticking valance (various colourways are available). It measures 194cm high x 75cm wide x 55cm deep. Also available are room and fire screens in four different designs. *Hoppé Design, The Bell House, Kingsland, Leominster, Hereford HR6 9RU. Tel.: 01568-708860.*

△ This 22-drawer pine chest is part of a completely new range of painted furniture offered by Grand Illusions. Each piece can be painted by hand in any two of some 400 possible colour combinations from their own paint range, or indeed supplied just waxed or unwaxed. The chest costs £495 waxed or £650 painted, plus delivery. Full details of the collection can be obtained from their new mail-order catalogue. *Grand Illusions, 2-4 Crown Rd, St. Margaret's, Twickenham, Middx TW1 3EE. Tel.: 0181-744 1046.*

△ A settle with a difference, this Game Cupboard is made from English elm and consists of a blanket chest and a cupboard with hanging racks, shelves and a gun-security cabinet. It costs £2,500. David Crews & Co. make a full range of furniture for the hall, study or kitchen, each piece being individually designed and handmade. *David Crews & Co., Church House, Ebberston, Scarborough, N. Yorks. YO13 9NR. Tel.: 01723-859751.*

▷ Rhode Design make two ranges of free-standing furniture in MDF. This painted cupboard comes from The Boston Collection and has a solid pine top. Measuring 83cm high x 84cm wide x 40cm deep, it is supplied ready to paint for £258, or painted for £412. Thirteen different pieces range from wardrobes to bedside tables. All the furniture can be adapted to individual needs, by *Rhode Design, 86 Stoke Newington Church St, London N16 OAP. Tel.: 0171-275 8261.*

CUPBOARDS AND CHESTS

◁ Reminiscent of the Bloomsbury Group, this wardrobe is hand-painted by John Gillah, who paints furniture to commission, starting at about £150. His company, Artifex, also produces a wide range of high-quality country-style furniture, made from pine and other hardwoods, skilfully painted with a distressed finish. Farmhouse dressers are a speciality, beautifully painted to look extremely old. Prices start at £695 for a standard open-top 1.5m dresser, though these pieces can be custom-made. Kitchens and Shaker-style pieces are also offered, as are home accessories such as glassware, hand-painted china, picture frames, and so on. There are two shops: *Artifex, 258 Royal Victoria Pl., Upper Mall, Tunbridge Wells, Kent TN1 2SS. Tel.: 01892-536630;* or *3 Vale Rd, Tunbridge Wells, Kent TN1 1BS. Tel.: 01892-549220.*

▽ A beautifully designed and crafted hi-fi cabinet from contemporary furniture designer Duncan Copley. Made of cherry with rosewood decoration, it reveals Duncan's close attention to detail. Drawers have been specially designed to store CDs and tapes, and there is even space for a treasured record collection. For prices and further information, contact *Duncan Copley Contemporary Furniture Design, The Old Co-op Yard, Clarence St, Ulverston, Cumbria LA12 7JJ. Tel.: 01229-580156/586447.*

▽ Robust and practical, Ben Casson's furniture is produced in solid timbers grown in the UK, oak being used for this bedside cabinet, which costs £390. Utilizing both traditional and innovative woodworking techniques, Ben makes chests of drawers, cabinets, tables, chairs, sideboards, bookshelves and garden furniture. Most of his pieces are made to order and Ben favours close contact with a client. *Ben Casson, Wobage Farm, Upton Bishop, Nr Ross-on-Wye, Hereford HR9 7QP. Tel.: 01989-780495.*

▷ Unmistakably English, this limed-oak castle cupboard is internally lit with glazed frosted glass. The whole stands on a Purbeck Stone plinth. This seven-year-old company (see also **Beds** and **Kitchens**) accepts both large and small contracts, custom-building to exacting standards fitted and free-standing furniture, kitchens, bedrooms and bathrooms, with strict attention to detail and liaising closely with a client. From concealed drawer runners to disguised lighting, Tim Wood controls space in thoughtful designs. Commissions include a fitted Tudor-arched kitchen in an old castle, accompanied by free-standing work. *Tim Wood Furniture Ltd, 41 Ballantine St, London SW18 1AL. Tel.: 0181-875 1638.*

▽ Jim Crockatt's magnificent oak chest, with walnut hinges and clasp, and measuring 1.2m x 90cm, testifies to his attempts to celebrate the beauty of wood, creating natural-looking pieces. Jim undertakes commissions ranging from blanket boxes to barns (see also **Tables and Chairs** and **Crafts for Children**), and prices are available on request. *Jim Crockatt, Pococks Cottage, Mariners Lane, Bradfield, Berks. RG7 6HX. Tel.: 01734-744728.*

◁ This tallboy is the work of interior designer Laurence J. Lewis, who has for many years designed furniture for his projects. The top and structural elements of the tallboy are crafted from solid maple, with sides and drawer fronts of matched maple veneer. Measuring 1.33m high x 1.26m wide x 46cm deep, it costs about £1,895. Each tallboy is made to order, with free delivery throughout mainland UK. *The Hand Made Tallboy Company, 16 Brookland Rise, London NW11 6DP. Tel.: 0181-458 9695.*

◁ John Makepeace Studio (see also **Tables and Chairs**) produces commissioned furniture of uncompromising quality, which explores the boundaries of tradition through imaginative and inventive structures. This open-frame set of drawers and tambour cabinet, 'Graduation', is made from hickory and burr olive-ash, with drawers lined in white vellum. Prices supplied on request. *John Makepeace Studio, Parnham House, Beaminster, Dorset DT8 3NA. Tel.: 01308-862204.*

▽ The beautifully painted *trompel'œil* books in this case are a fine example of the work of decorative artist and copyist, Niggy Thomas (see also **Tables and Chairs** and **Paint Effects**). He works to commission and specializes in creating complex effects. For further information, contact *Niggy Thomas 18 Ashmount Rd, London N19 3BJ. Tel.: 0171-272 6078* or *01625-525205.*

Steve Allen Cabinet Makers, *Hollin Bridge Mill, Hollin Bridge St, Blackburn, Lancs. BB2 4BB (Tel.: 01254-54146),* build attractive free-standing bookcases and reproduction dressers.

Bridge House Carpentry and Joinery, *Bridge House, Mill Lane, Alhampton, Nr Shepton Mallet, Somerset BA4 6PX (Tel.: 01749-860620),* make a specialist fishing cabinet in solid mahogany to order.

Codrington Furniture *(Tel.: 0171-498 9960)* manufacture a range of handsome traditional furniture including a Shaker-style counter with a polished cherry top and distressed paint finish.

Lovelace, *Broad Piece, Soham, Cambridge CB7 5EL (Tel.: 01353-721339),* produce timeless pieces, such as a drinks cabinet, writing bureau and corner cupboard.

Mark Rowan Furniture, *Garreg Fawr, Porthyrhyd, Llanwrda, Dyfed SA19 8NY (Tel.: 01558-650478),* deal in antique and painted furniture.

Somerset Country, *779 Fulham Rd, London SW6 5HA (Tel.: 0171-371 0436),* specialize in country-style furniture – hand-painted cupboards, dressers and armoires with fabric doors.

Star Furniture, *25 Shacklewell St, London E2 7EG (Tel.: 0171-729*

7079); Fiona Clark works to commission, making colourful eclectic pieces, and sells a small range of CD cabinets.

Thistle Joinery Ltd, *77 Ilderton Rd, Bermondsey, London SE16 3JZ (Tel.: 0171-232 1553),* make a range of bookcases, including break-front and Gothic styles, and a home office, with integrated table and bookcase.

▽ Floor-to-ceiling shelving with Gothic arches by Hayloft Woodwork, specially designed to hold music, hi-fi and CDs in the organ scholar's room at Girton College, Cambridge. A 12-year-old joinery business specializing in custom-made furniture, including alcove bookcases, wardrobes, beds, desks and radiator covers, Hayloft Woodwork also produce a wide range of traditional kitchen, bedroom and bathroom designs. (See also **Kitchen Accessories**.) Most of their work is in old pine and a variety of hardwoods, and MDF, an ideal surface for painted or specialist finishes. All their furniture is handmade to order to a high standard of craftsmanship and is available plain or painted in any finish. Contact *Hayloft Woodwork, 3 Bond St (off Chiswick High Rd), London W4 1QZ. Tel.: 0181-747 3510.*

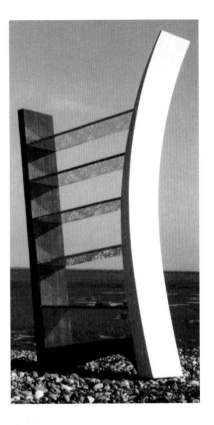

△ The bowed sides and combination of textures in this set of wood and glass shelves are typical features of the work of innovative furniture designer Duncan Copley. Working mostly to commission, Duncan produces a huge range of designs from his workshop in Cumbria (see also **Cupboards and Chests** and **Upholstered Furniture**). For prices and further information, contact *Duncan Copley Contemporary Furniture Design, The Old Co-op Yard, Clarence St, Ulverston, Cumbria LA12 7JJ. Tel.: 01229 580156 /586447.*

Small Furniture

Whether you're seeking an elegant answer to a practical problem or have one of those intractable spaces in your house, a small piece of furniture may provide the solution.

SMALL FURNITURE

▷ Extremely versatile, this rattan tray with hand-painted folding legs can be used in the bathroom for soaps and towels, for picnics in the garden or as an occasional table in the sitting-room. It measures 66cm high x 62cm long x 44cm wide, and costs £158. To order, contact *George Clark, The High St, Stockbridge, Hants SO20 6HF. Tel.: 01264-811044.*

▽ The laminated construction of these music stands makes them not only slim and graceful but also strong and stable. They are handmade by Neil Wyn Jones at Artizana (see also **Tables and Chairs** and **Silver**) in virtually any timber (shown here in ebony and lacewood). The stands adjust, from 70 to 125cm, to allow sitting or standing, and prices start at £360. *Artizana, The Village, Prestbury, Cheshire SK10 4DG. Tel.: 01625-827582.*

△ Julian Coode designs and makes these small tables, carefully considering the cylindrical space beneath the circular top. By monopolizing the strength of forged mild steel, he makes it describe this otherwise unused space, while also ensuring a strong supportive structure. Glass tops enable the viewer to appreciate the framework below. Each table costs £200, and stands 70cm high. Julian has produced one-off commissions for private clients, architects and local authorities. *Julian Coode, Nailbourne Forge, Littlebourne, Canterbury, Kent CT3 1TX. Tel.: 01227-728336.*

◁ This mirrored cabinet is made by Cas Stanier (see also **Mirrors**), who specializes in diverse gilding effects, such as *verre eglomisé*, complemented with lacquerwork and inlays. The cabinet, constructed in painted wood and gilded glass, contains a glass shelf ideal for display purposes and costs £900. Contact *Cas Stanier, Tel.: 0171-229 8017.*

SMALL FURNITURE

▽ A Club Fender, made-to-measure by Acres Farm (see also **Decorative Accessories**). Handmade by their own team of craftsmen, the fenders come in brass, steel, copper or wood, or in a mixture of materials. The seating is covered in leather, in a choice of six standard colours, though others are possible. Flame-retardant fabric, supplied by a customer, can also be fitted. An extensive colour brochure of fenders is available, together with extremely simple instructions on how to measure a fireplace, though a country-wide measuring service is also offered. Prices start at about £450 for a simple black steel fender. Contact *Acres Farm, Bradfield, Reading, Berks. RG7 6JH. Tel.: 01734-744305.*

◁ Handmade by Dorset craftsmen and hand-painted in a choice of seven traditional colours, the 'Milton Abbas Table' works as a lamp table and suits the bathroom, too. It measures 67.5cm high x 40cm wide and costs £149, available from Orchard. This shop specializes in contemporary country furniture and accessories such as cupboards, tables and a food larder (see **Kitchen Accessories**). Also pottery and soft furnishings. *Orchard, 14 Mill Lane, Wimborne, Dorset BH21 1LN. Tel.: 01202-848849.*

▽ Depicting some of New York's finest buildings, this screen contains many thousands of pieces of veneer, each one cut by hand and pieced into the whole. Typical of the outstanding marquetry skills practised by craftsmen at David Linley Furniture, the screen stands 2.1m high and 3.6m wide. Founded in 1985, this company's commissions range from domestic furniture to huge pieces, and the key to their success is individual attention. They also make small items for the home: desk accessories, tableware, boxes and mirrors, to name but a few. Prices accommodate a range of budgets. Contact *David Linley Furniture Ltd, 60 Pimlico Rd, London SW1W 8LP. Tel.: 0171-730 7300.*

◁ Crafted in the 18thC manner, with lightweight wooden frames finished with wet paper stretched across the batons, the screens by The Felbrigg Design Company (see also **Decorative Fixtures**) are upholstered. They can be made up in the company's wide range of fabrics so that they cost from £250, or in a covering supplied by a client, costing from £130 (including upholstery and trimmings). Many different sizes and shapes are available from stock; commissions are gladly undertaken. *The Felbrigg Design Company, The Coach House, 4 Park La., Sutton Benger, Wilts. SN15 4RN. Tel.: 01249-720076.*

△ Working solely to commission and employing wood, glass and metalwork, Cara Crawley designs and makes a wide variety of items, both large and small, such as candelabra, mirrors, tables, wall-hangings and screens. This screen is made from gesso on board, with graphite and oil, and measures approximately 2m square. Screens start at £850, though Cara especially enjoys working to a large scale. For further details, contact *Cara Crawley, 228 Hammersmith Grove, London W6 7HG. Tel.: 0181-749 7739.*

△ Entitled 'In a Bright Sunlit Garden', this room-dividing screen is made by Amanda Pearce (see also **Decorative Accessories**). Colour is an essential ingredient of Amanda's work, as this piece testifies. Several layers and textures are created by paper being ripped and cut up, then imprinted with ink, and further coloured with oil pastels. Both screens and collages are offered, with screens starting at £500. *Amanda Pearce, 74 Carlingford Rd, Hucknall, Notts. NG15 7AG. Tel.: 0115-963 8440.*

◁ Screen Scene is run by two sisters, Alison Buchanan and Camilla Clark, who supply room screens at reasonable prices. Custom-made from blockboard (durable and light), the screens consist of any number of panels and come in four standard designs, covered in the fabric of your choice and finished with braid. A standard panel of 170 x 40cm costs £59. Alternatively, kits are sold, with blockboard frames (for covering with wallpaper, découpage or fabric) or MDF (for painting or stencilling), which cost £29 per panel and come with brass hinges, screws and simple instructions for covering. Contact *Screen Scene, The Garden House, Mountstephen, Uffculme, Devon EX15 3BX. Tel.: 01884-841044.*

Upholstered Furniture

Fine furniture, elegantly dressed, that owes its good looks as much to the skills of the tailor as it does to those of the joiner.

The Kilim Furniture Company sources its kilims in Turkey, selecting them for quality, design, colour and wearability, before employing them to cover specially-made upholstered furniture. Experienced craftsmen make Knole sofas, ottomans, club chairs, daybeds, stools and so on in traditional English designs, and use carefully selected kiln-dried beech for sofa and chair frames. (All materials are fire-retardant and cushions are filled with duck feathers.) Kilim-covered furniture is available from stock, though a custom-made service is also offered, allowing customers to select their own kilim covering from the wide range held. Furniture can also be produced to commission in virtually any size and style, and in the fabric of your choice. Kilim-covered prices: stools £330-450; club chair £1,150; two-seater sofa £2,150; three-seater sofa £2,750; from *Kilim Furniture Co., 88 Hendon Lane, London N3 3SL. Tel.: 0181-343 3487.*

Upholstered Furniture

△ The Ferrera sofa is a fine example of the bespoke sofas and upholstered items designed and made by Laurence J. Lewis, available as individual pieces or as part of a complete conceptual project. Sprung and stitched by hand in the traditional manner by his own craftsmen, the furniture combines fine upholstery skills with contemporary styling. This sofa measures 1.8m long, requires 8m of fabric and costs about £1,975, from *Laurence J. Lewis, 16 Brookland Rise, London NW11 6DP. Tel.: 0181-458 9695.*

▽ A pair of exquisitely carved and gilded armchairs, part of a suite designed to replace the originals, made in about 1800. They are on public display at Powderham Castle, Exeter, home of the Earl of Devon. Longpré Cabinet Makers specialize in finest-quality replicas of period furniture and, as bespoke craftsmen, they can also design and make contemporary-style pieces. *Longpré Cabinet Makers, Hatherleigh Farm, Wincanton, Somerset BA9 8AB. Tel.: 01963-34356.*

△ A selection of luxurious sofas and armchairs from Simply Chic. Covers are loose, machine-washable, made from 100% Jacquard cotton, and come in a choice of 17 eye-catching colours. Internally, all the sofas and armchairs are fully coil-sprung, with fire-proof carcasses. Frames, crafted from Scandinavian beech, are solidly screwed, doweled and glued together. Cushions are duck feather- and down-filled. Armchairs start at £565; sofas at £725; three- and four- seaters are available. Simply Chic are at *46 The Quadrant, Richmond, Surrey TW9 1DN. Tel.: 0181-940 5151* and at *The Plaza, 535 Kings Rd, London SW10 0TZ. Tel.: 0171-352 6931.*

▽ The Rococo sofa is designed and manufactured by Ann and Christopher Hymers, and is part of a collection of sofas, chairs and stools. Combining style with comfort, their furniture can be dismantled for easy access. Hand-crafted, it is available in a huge choice of fabrics and can also incorporate loose covers. This sofa costs £795, plus 10m of fabric. Curtain-making and interior design services are also offered. Their shop (closed Mon. only) is at *Intermura, 27 Chalk Farm Rd, London NW1 8AG. Tel.: 0171-485 6638.*

UPHOLSTERED FURNITURE

◁ Robust and colourful, these stools are designed and made by Roger Oates Designs (see also **Flooring**), who offer a choice of traditional or contemporary looks. The pieces are upholstered in designs from their range of 100% wool flat-weave floor coverings. A footstool measures 40 x 40 x 22cm and costs £89; a long stool 60 x 40 x 40cm, for £155; and a table-bench 120 x 40 x 40cm, for £189. (Prices include fabric.) For mail-order details, contact *Roger Oates Design Associates, The Long Barn, Eastnor, Ledbury, Hereford HR8 1EL. Tel.: 01531-632718.*

▽ A well-established shop of kilim-covered furniture, George Smith stocks a number of covered sofas, chairs and footstools, as well as piles of old kilims from which customers can choose covers. All the furniture is hand-crafted and hand-sprung, and cushions are filled with duck feather and down. This standard chair is available in small, medium and large, costing the same whatever the size: £1,762.50. The large version, as illustrated, measures 85cm high x 84cm wide x 109cm deep. Footstools cost £587.50. Sofas up to 2m in length start at £3,290; over 2m, £4,112.50. All the furniture is available in a choice of other fabrics, too, for a different price. For more information, contact *George Smith, 587/589 Kings Rd, London SW6 2EH. Tel.: 0171-384 1004.*

UPHOLSTERED FURNITURE

▽ Balmain & Balmain sell custom-made upholstered sofas and chairs through agents, offering a broad range of designs and sizes, such as this large two-seater Avon sofa, which starts at £650, depending on the fabric. The furniture is built on beech frames and incorporates coil-sprung seats and either coil-sprung or cushion backs. Feather cushions come as standard, though other fillings are available. For information on stockists, contact *Balmain & Balmain, The Old Rectory, Sandford Orcas, Sherborne, Dorset DT9 4SB. Tel.: 01963-220247.*

▽ Skilled craftsmen at Pier Fagan make traditional sofas and armchairs to order, using only natural materials. The range consists of drop-arm sofas and chesterfields; armchairs, stools and so on. The company will upholster in any fabric supplied by a customer, at no extra cost. Sofas start at £575. The showroom is open seven days a week, by appointment only. *Pier Fagan, 132 Bermondsey St, London SE1 3TX. Tel.: 0171-403 5585.*

▷ Made to order, the Toulouse Chair by Derwent Upholstery is hand-crafted from beech and has an upholstered back and front, and a separate seat cushion. The choice of finishes offered is American cherry, antique ivory, dappled walnut and (as shown) Provençal Green. The frames are made to varying designs, and prices start at £660, plus 3.5m of fabric. *Derwent Upholstery, Greenhill Industrial Estate, Greenhill Lane, Riddings, Derbs. DE55 4BR. Tel.: 01773-604121.*

△ The Alexandra sofa is the latest addition to Beaumont & Fletcher's range of upholstered chairs, sofas and stools, all made by hand, employing traditional methods. Shown here in their Alexius granite-green fabric (£38 per m), the sofa costs £1,485, plus 10m of fabric. For more information, contact *Beaumont & Fletcher, 98 Waterford Rd, London SW6 2HA. Tel.: 0171-384 2642.*

▷ A self-taught furniture designer, Duncan Copley explores boundaries with his inspiring, modern furniture. He usually employs native hardwoods, complemented with unusual paint finishes, and textures created by adding metal, glass and ceramic. This 'Tusk' chair costs £890, plus 4m of fabric. Duncan works largely to commission, offering a broad variety of designs, such as cabinets with curved lines. *Duncan Copley Contemporary Furniture Design, The Old Co-op Yard, Clarence St, Ulverston, Cumbria LA12 7JJ. Tel.: 01229-580156/586447.*

▽ A leading specialist in the design and manufacture of upholstered stools and ottomans, Philida Cross produces a standard range, but can also make to order, with a customer's choice of fabric. Small footstools for covering in tapestries and needlework are also offered. Overall, this window seat is 68cm high x 127cm long and costs £345, plus 3m of fabric + p & p. The button-backed footstool is 38cm high x 114cm long, costing £265, plus 2m of fabric + p & p, from *Essential Items, Church House, Plungar, Nottingham NG13 0JA. Tel.: 01949-861172 .*

△ Based near Edinburgh, Clock House Furniture design and make a huge range of high-quality stools. They not only maintain and develop standard styles, offering a wealth of finishes, sizes and traditional and contemporary designs, in the fabric of your choice, but also welcome commissions to virtually any requirements. This stool can double as a coffee-table, measuring 110 x 85cm and costs £320, excluding fabric. For a colour brochure, contact *Clock House Furniture, The Old Stables, Overhailes, Haddington, E. Lothian EH41 3SB. Tel.: 01620-861300.*

▽ Based on an original mid-19thC design, this miniature *chaise-longue* (1.7m long) was made to commission by Rupert Bevan (see also **Mirrors**) and consists of a hand-painted and gilded beech frame. Rupert specializes in adapting antique designs and works closely with a client to produce a (cheaper) version of his own. He and his skilled team of craftsmen work to commission only, and to almost any budget, starting at around £500, to produce a wide selection of furniture. They also offer a restoration service. *Rupert Bevan, 40 Fulham High St, London SW6 3LQ. Tel.: 0171-731 1919.*

Beds

Insomniacs aside, most of us spend about 3,000 hours a year in bed. Time invested in choosing the right one – whether it's a four poster, a brass or a feather bed – is well spent.

◁ Subtle curves and gracious style give this four poster bed a light unobtrusive presence. Romantically draped in soft French voile, it is the work of Stephen Owen, artist, designer and craftsman. Made from imbuia – Brazilian walnut – from sustainable woodlands, it is solid yet smooth to the touch. Two attached cabinets provide storage, and small reading lights are built into the head rail. Stephen specializes in one-off pieces of furniture and commissions, working directly with his clients. The bed costs £29,375. Contact *Stephen Owen, Whipley Studio, Whipley Manor Farm, Bramley, Surrey GU5 0LL. Tel.: 01483-278309.*

▷ Curving, simple lines characterize this supremely elegant bed by innovative furniture designer Tim Wood. Crafted from sycamore and decorated with American black walnut carved star motifs, it is made to order, to any size and individual specification. Well-known for his designs for specialist kitchens, bedrooms and bathrooms, which can be fitted or free-standing to suit individual requirements, Tim works in close collaboration with his clients and pays an attention to detail which goes beyond the merely aesthetic. For prices and further details, contact *Tim Wood Furniture, 41 Ballantine St, London SW18 1AL. Tel.: 0181-875 1638.*

◁ Strikingly smart and sophisticated, this headboard from a range by Toby Winteringham measures 90 x 150cm, is made of Burr Elm with rope marquetry, designed to give a *trompe l'œil* effect, and rosewood columns, topped by traditional gilded bedknobs. Prices are from £850 + VAT. Order from *Toby Winteringham, Whitehouse, Bawsey, King's Lynn, Norfolk PE32 1EY. Tel.: 01553-841829.*

BEDS

▷ One in the delightful range of restored antique pine and painted sleigh beds from Harriet Ann Beds. Its characteristic high sides, originally designed to keep out draughts, make the sleigh an ideal first bed for a child. Harriet Ann Beds import the finest of these unusual beds, made only between 1890 and 1930 and now much sought-after, from Scandinavia and other parts of Europe. For prices and further details, contact *Harriet Ann Beds, Standen Farm, Smarden Rd, Biddenden, Nr Ashford, Kent TN27 8JT. Tel. 01580-291220.*

▷ Whales and crests of waves are the motifs decorating this solid wooden bed, part of a range of handmade furniture by Joseph Falconer. From his shop in Highbury, he makes to order unusual naive country-style furniture with a twist, in grainy reclaimed timber. Telephone for further information and, to see Joseph's full range of furniture, visit his shop, *The Barn, 238 St. Paul's Rd, London N1 2LJ. Tel.: 0171-359 1614.*

◁ The skilled craftsmen employed by The Iron Bed Company use many old casting techniques, but modern painting processes ensure a more durable finish. All the beds in their collection are available as bedsteads, surrounds, which fit around an existing divan, and headboards, come in any size – even non-standard – and a choice of colours. The 'Tosca', left, costs £469 for a double, including sprung slatted base. Visit their shop in Puttenham near Guildford, but phone first (*Tel.: 01483-810886*), or their factory, *The Iron Bed Company, Southfield Park, Delling Lane, Old Bosham, W. Sussex PO18 8NN. Tel.: 01243-574049.*

▽ An eye-catching double bed (150 x 195cm) made of steel with coloured glass spheres by designer and metalsmith Adrian Reynolds. He produces a range of contemporary furniture and accessories, undertakes commissions for architects and interior designers, and has exhibited his work widely in the UK and abroad. This bed costs £1,410 and can be ordered from *Adrian Reynolds, Tel./Fax.: 01952-433222.*

△ Europe's leading specialist in French and classical wooden beds, Simon Horn offers over 60 traditional designs, from the simplicity of the *Lit Bateau* to splendidly dressed four posters and this dramatic Venetian Bed. His antique copies are all handmade from solid wood. Clients can choose from a variety of woods – including rose and cherry – and can specify both the stain and patina. Also available is the new metamorphic Simon Horn Cot. A unique design based on a classic *Lit Bateau*, it starts life as a traditional cot, then becomes a child's bed, and finally a sofa. Mattresses and divans are made to order, with unusual sizes a speciality. *Simon Horn Furniture, 117-121 Wandsworth Bridge Rd, London SW6 2TP. Tel.: 0171-731 1279.*

BEDS

◁ One of over 2,000 examples of antique brass and iron bedsteads available at Bed Bazaar, specialist antique metal bedstead dealers. A huge variety of styles and sizes are displayed, both restored, in the showroom, and untouched, in the Suffolk barn warehouse. They stock the full range of Sleeping Partners mattresses and specialist bases; any size and shape to order. Mail order available. Contact *Bed Bazaar, The Old Station Building, Station Rd, Framlingham, Suffolk IP13 9EE. Tel.: 01728-723756.*

△ Remembering the warmth and sheer comfort of her grandmother's feather bed, Annie Elliott started making her own feather-filled mattresses, and in due course set up The Feather Bed Company. Each mattress is handmade in her Devon workshop from a double layer of best English feather-proof cotton ticking and generously filled with curled duck feathers. Prices start at £225 for a single mattress. Non-standard sizes, bolsters and pillows are also available, and a delivery service. *The Feather Bed Company, Crosslands House, Ash Thomas, Tiverton, Devon EX16 4NU. Tel.: 01884-821331.*

△ An ingenious space-saving idea, Hoppé Design's Bed in a Box is ideal for putting up occasional guests. The bed has a three-fold mechanism and 70 x 180cm foam mattress. The box is available in four plain colourways, the customer's own fabric, or antique pine. It is 85 x 67 x 42cm and can be used as an ottoman, coffee table or seat. A delivery service covers the UK and Europe. Hoppé also make screens, pelmets and a tented wardrobe (see **Cupboards and Chests**). *Hoppé Design, The Bell House, Kingsland, Leominster, Hereford HR6 9RU. Tel.: 01568-708860.*

Ceramics

The following pages overflow with colourful pots, plates, dishes, bowls, jugs, vases and vessels, thrown and painted by hand, raku-fired or sgraffito-decorated.

◁ More than 30 different breeds of sheep and other farm animals decorate these charming mugs in fine bone china designed by Jane Healey, who appropriately keeps cattle and sheep. The mugs are available by mail order at £3.60 each + p & p from *Mrs Jane Healey, 32 Down Park Cottages, West Harting, Nr Petersfield, Hants. GU31 5PF. Tel.: 01730-821646.* Send an s.a.e. for an illustrated brochure.

▽ Influenced by sturdy early English pottery and the vitality of Cretan Minoan ware, Joanna Still's work shows her feeling for landscape. She uses red earthenware clay, dipped in a creamy slip and painted before the first firing. The final glaze is fired to 1,080°C revealing a wide range of warm colours; see the plates below, which cost £33 each from *4 Beckford Cottages, Hindon, Salisbury, Wilts. SP3 6ED. Tel.: 01747-820478.*

△ Drawing her inspiration from many sources including architecture, wildlife and floral images, Wendy Johnson builds all her individual ceramics by hand, using slab, pinch and modelling techniques. Colours – deep blues, powdery greens, yellows and subtle pinks – are also inspired by nature. Illustrated is just a sample of her range (the clock costs £157; small vase, £58; and large vase £85). Wendy also works to commission. *Tel.: 0115-9607940.*

▷ Jessica Ball uses thin slabs of white earthenware, cut and curled, to create functional, but also highly decorative one-off pieces, ranging from a single jug to a whole coffee service (the one illustrated costs £140). Bold patterns, vivid colours and the sparkle of the gold lustre she applies to much of her work, give a crisp bright finish. Jessica accepts commissions. Contact her at *12 River St, Haworth, W. Yorks. BD22 8ND. Tel.: 01535-647221.*

▽ Striking, colourful ceramics and textiles produced by Yerja Ceramics & Textiles, the partnership of studio potter, Chris Speyer, and textile designer, Kath Ukleja. Chris makes oxidation-fired stoneware, which includes large thrown and pressed platters, slab-built animals, elaborate candlesticks, wall decorations and exuberant tableware. Prices range from £15 to £300. The partners undertake large-scale commissions, and also exhibit regularly in galleries and at selected craft fairs. Their showroom is open to visitors (telephone first), and a mail-order service is provided. Contact *Yerja Ceramics & Textiles, Mill Rise, Ford Rd, Bampton, Devon EX16 9LW. Tel.: 01398-331163.*

△ Splashes of colour from the Mediterranean, traces of Ancient Greece, Matisse-inspired figures in flowing lines and a hint of humour are hallmarks of Karen Atherley's striking ceramics. She creates large one-off pieces – vases, bowls, plates and centrepieces – as well as numerous cups, saucers and teapots. Prices range from £12 to £120. Order in writing from *Karen Atherley, 4 Tower Ct, Thorney, Peterborough PE6 0PW. Tel.: 01733-270330.*

▷ Texture and colour are key components of Vivienne Foley's wheel-thrown porcelain, from paper-thin bowls to large vases, such as her elegant 36cm-tall 'Cobalt Vase with Bronze'. A strong oriental influence is evident both in her designs and the new glazes she has developed. Contact Vivienne at *33 Denholme Rd, London W9 3HT. Tel.: 0181-964 8537.*

▽ Lucy Howard's playful, whimsical ceramics are decorative variations on common domestic themes (see her Spotty Teaset £65, Teatime Teapot £75, and Spiral Dish £75). Her inspiration stems both from everyday surroundings – colours, patterns, ordinary and bizarre objects – and from different countries and cultures – their architecture and free use of colour and decoration. Contact Lucy at *34 Vestris Rd, Forest Hill, London SE23 2EE. Tel.: 0181-699 1007.*

△ Penelope Patrick's vibrantly colourful abstract and figurative ceramics are hand-sculpted or thrown in terracotta, beige or white earthenware clay. Prices start at £10. Special personalized sets or pieces can be ordered from *Penelope Patrick Travelling Pottery. Tel./Fax: 0171-223 7559.*

◁ Working from the kitchen of her old stone cottage, Wilma Allan makes elegant pots, employing the ancient method of coiling, slowly building up the form by adding coils of clay. Before they are dry, she burnishes them to a smooth sheen with a pebble. She uses no glazes or unnatural colour and achieves swirling grey and black patterns by smoking the pots in sawdust in a kiln. The one illustrated costs £130 from *Wilma Allan, Graig Ddu, Llanthony, Abergavenny, Gwent NP7 7NW. Tel.: 01873-890723.*

▽ Sylph Baier throws in traditional red earthenware and hand-paints her attractive pots, using majolica techniques. Her 'Storm in a Teacup' range has its origins in Brighton and was developed from sketching trips to Shoreham harbour. It includes a four-cup teapot (£64), cone cups (£18.50 each), a variety of bowls, mugs and plates. Not shown below are children's cups with names on (£11), lighthouse storage jars (£48) and a large pasta jar (£84). Sylph will personalize items at no extra cost. She also makes shell lightpulls in eight colours (£7.95 each), and welcomes commissions. Her work can be bought by mail order or from the showroom at *Tin Star Studio, 38 Cheltenham Pl., Brighton BN1 4AB. Tel.: 01273-682042.*

▷ Sally Bourne's colourful 'Bobbing Fish' vase (£56 + p & p) is part of an ever-increasing range that includes clocks, mugs, lightpulls, mirrors and bathroom accessories. Sally uses a unique method of surface decoration, hand-casting each piece and then decorating it with porcelain slips, overlaid and scratched through to produce practical yet decorative vitrified ware. Contact *Sally Bourne Ceramics, 1d Orleston Rd, London N7 8LH. Tel.: 0171-700 6642.*

▷ Sally Reilly's sophisticated Festival series of tableware was inspired by a 1950s bathroom and by slip-coloured beer mugs once used in pubs. Each piece is hand-thrown and available in yellow, pink and blue, colours which work well alone or combined. Prices range from £8 to £24. Sally makes another range of tableware called Sienna. Visit her showroom by appointment or order by mail: *Lyndhurst Studios, 92 Station Rd, Soham, Ely, Cambs. CB7 5DZ. Tel.: 01223-510638.*

▽ Fresh and contemporary, yet with the warmth and feel of country slipware, Sean Miller's hand-thrown and slipped earthenware pottery includes mugs, jugs, candlesticks, plates, oven dishes and large bowls. All his work is designed for practical kitchen or table use, is dishwasher-proof and hardwearing. Prices range from about £12 for a mug to £75 for a large bowl. For further details and stockists, contact Sean on *Tel.: 0181-208 0148.*

△ Spots, stripes and checks, in bold Italian-inspired colours, decorate Piggery Pottery's exciting handmade earthenware designs. These include fruit, salad and pasta bowls, teapots, jugs, mugs and plates, costing from £5.50 for a mug to £35 for a large fruit bowl. Contact *Piggery Pottery, Grange Barn, Grange Rd, Wareham, Dorset BH20 5AL. Tel.: 01929-554136.* They are also happy to accept commissions.

◁ A specialist shop in Harrogate, Porcellana sells wonderful hand-crafted and painted Italian ceramica. Pieces range from mugs, decorated with fruit (£8.50 + p & p), to 'Celestial' plates with gold-leaf suns, stars, moons and planets applied by hand (£35-40 + p & p). They also stock attractive bathroom accessories. Available through their retail outlets and mail order: *Porcellana, 63 Station Parade, Harrogate, N. Yorks. HG1 1ST. Tel.: 01423-500030.*

▽ Founded in 1952, Chelsea Pottery has become famous for the sgraffito drawing and jewel-coloured glazes used to decorate their ceramics. Sgraffito is a technique in which the design is scratched in by the artist. A small group of people work to produce unique, handmade vases, bowls, plates, jugs and other pieces, mostly decorated with the Pottery's traditional flower and animal designs (prices range from £29.60 for the trumpet vase to £49.90 for the jug both illustrated). They also make commemmorative plates, house-name plaques, garden sculptures, and their now-famous caricatures of barristers and judges. They are happy to discuss commissions. Visit or contact *Chelsea Pottery, 5 Ebury Mews, London SW1W 9NX. Tel.: 0171-259 0164.*

◁ Influenced by antique country pottery and 18th-19thC Staffordshire groups, David and Margaret Cleverly specialize in animals, which they make individually from red clay. Like this turkey (£132), most of their animals are farmyard or domestic, with the occasional circus lion or tiger. They also produce a range of coloured domestic pottery (prices £4.50-£89). Contact *Haytown Pottery, Haytown, Holsworthy, Devon EX22 7UW. Tel.: 01409-261476.*

▽ A simple attractive design, these soap dishes and toothbrush mugs, decorated with shells, will fit happily into almost any bathroom. They come in the three colourways illustrated – blue, green and mottled – and are available by mail order, as a matching set for £23 or individually, the soap dish for £12.99 and the toothbrush mug for £11.99. Add £1.50 p & p per order. Contact *Liza Gardner Ceramics, Adorno's Hut, 96c Bedford Hill, London SW12 9HR. Tel.: 0181-673 2022.*

◁ Inspired by ancient art and archaeology, Jo Firth creates unique pieces of ceramic art, in the form of bottles, bowls and hanging moon vessels. Her stunning Persian blue crackle-glazed bottle (38cm high and £180) is raku-fired, a technique dating from 16thC Japan. Each piece is fired individually, removed from the kiln at the top temperature and smoked in sawdust to give rich crackle and lustre finishes. Contact *Jo Firth, Dorncliffe, Burden's Heath, Upper Bucklebury, Nr Reading, Berks. RG7 6SX. Tel.: 01635-861326.*

▷ Influenced by designs in tin and pewter, Steve Harrison's jugs in attractive muted colours are thrown and rolled with pressed spouts and handles. Made from white stoneware and salt-glazed to 1,300°C, the tallest measures 17cm and the smallest, 5cm. Steve welcomes commissions. For prices and further information, contact him at *40 Brodie Rd, Enfield, Middx EN2 0ET. Tel.: 0181-482 4169.*

△ Onglaze is a specialist shop, established in 1992 by Tim and Marissa Weatherhead to sell their own designs which, as their Summer Fruit range shows, combine the traditional shapes of fine bone china with fresh, free, colourful paintwork. The range does not stop at the designs displayed in the shop and catalogue; any name or motif can be painted on to any piece, creating personal, original gifts. Prices start at £8.50 for a mug. *Onglaze, 46 Harrington Rd, London SW7 3ND. Tel.: 0171-823 8483.*

▷ Wendy Suffield collects Staffordshire china cow creamers, which she displays in her house. Right, is the attractive version that she sells in her shop, The Hambledon Gallery (see below). This creamer is available in four colourways, and costs £39.95. Contact *The Hambledon Gallery, 42-44 Salisbury St, Blandford Forum, Dorset DT11 7PR. Tel.: 01258-452880.*

◁ Wendy Suffield's shop, The Hambledon Gallery in Blandford Forum, Dorset, is an Aladdin's Cave of treasures. This glorious distressed blue country dresser (for sale at the gallery) is loaded with blue and white china, including Brixton Pottery, Creamware, china by Villeroy & Boch and Burgess & Leigh, and white china from ICTC, all obtainable from the shop; as are the silk flowers by Sia. Wendy also stocks mirrors, furniture, clothes, jewellery, kitchen accessories and garden ornaments (see **The Garden**), and stages exhibitions of work by acclaimed artists. Visit or telephone *The Hambledon Gallery, 42-44 Salisbury St, Blandford Forum, Dorset DT11 7PR. Tel.: 01258-452880.*

▽ Millennium's White Wicker collection is a range of well-designed, versatile porcelain tableware with a white-on-white embossed border pattern. Simple, yet sophisticated, it is as appropriate for a dinner party as it is for breakfast. For prices and stockists, contact *Millennium Tableware Ltd, 7 Swallow Pl., London W1R 7AD. Tel.: 0171-493 3313.* See also **Glass**.

△ Mel Cartwright loves strong rich colours and unusual designs, realized in her colourful hand-painted ceramics. Her designs range from complete tea services to the 'fish' pot with lid and toast rack illustrated. Every piece is stamped with Mel's distinctive style. Favourite designs include fish, cats, multi-coloured stripes and lilac roses. Her images are quirkily primitive and often humorous. Although her work is always decorative, Mel never loses sight of the function of a piece. To order, contact *Cartwright Ceramics, Blue Cat House Studios, 10A & 11 Howard Rd, Brighton, E. Sussex BN2 2TP. Tel.: 01273-700370.*

CERAMICS

▽ Actress Holly Aird has recently turned her hobby, painting ceramics, into a sideline. Using watercolours to achieve a matt finish, Holly chooses strong colours or rich pastels, and gold and silver contribute to all her work. Favourite motifs are mosaic dots, stars and hearts, although she will work to commission on other designs. Shown here are a small flower pot (£20), a heart-shaped box (£35), a flower plate (£22.50), a tile (£12) and letters of the alphabet (£7.50 each). For more information contact Holly on *Fax: 01273-487615.*

▷ Every piece of Morgen Hall's handmade tableware is a unique shape and pattern, so you can create a new table setting for each meal. Morgen makes a wide range, from tea cabarets and breakfast sets to 90cm-high storage jars and sterling silver cutlery. Prices start at £26 for a mug. Contact Morgen at *Studio 5, Chapter Arts Centre, Market Rd, Canton, Cardiff CF5 1QE. Tel.: 01222-396061 ext. 219* or *01222-238716.*

© Dewi Lloyd

© Dug Falby

▽ Suzanne Katkhuda's stunning flower designs are one of the many ranges of exquisite hand-painted ceramics that she produces. Others include the bright and zany Dots and Dashes in pretty pastels, the primitive African-inspired Earth Songs, in rich natural colours, the humorous country Farmyard collection, and the fiery landscapes of the Fauve. There is a wide choice of pieces in each design, from bowls, plates, cups, saucers and mugs, to platters, jugs, candlesticks, plant pots and storage jars. All are dishwasher-proof and microwave-safe. For further information, prices and stockists, *Tel.: 01604-880800/ Fax: 01604-880884.*

▷ Inspired by the simple beauty of ancient pottery, Emma Falcke's distinctive ceramics combine style, flair and practicality. Working in stoneware clay and with assorted copper glazes, she creates wonderful pots for the home and garden. This jug is 45cm high and costs £150. For more information on her collection, contact Emma at *Studio One, 1 Victoria St, Rochester, Kent ME1 1XJ. Tel.: 01634-811469.*

CERAMICS

▽ In an idyllic Cornish setting, internationally acclaimed ceramist Paul Jackson makes striking pieces in slipped terracotta, to which he then applies a range of techniques, such as sgraffito decoration, sponging, spraying and hand-painting. Much of his work reveals his passion for gardening and other autobiographical details. Prices range between £8 and £800. Contact Paul or visit his showroom by appointment: *Helland Bridge Pottery, Helland Bridge, Nr Bodmin, Cornwall PL30 4QR. Tel.: 01208-75240.*

◁ Stripes, spirals and sunflowers inspire the decoration of Sophie Hamilton's plant pots. Made of stoneware, the pots are all hand-decorated, using various techniques to apply layers of rich brightly coloured glazes. The range also includes mugs, jugs, bowls, plates and vases (prices range from £4 to £70; the small plant pot is £8.40, the medium size £12), and can be bought from *Sophie Hamilton, Deerholme Pottery, High Marishes, Malton, N. Yorks. YO17 0UQ. Tel.: 01653-668228.*

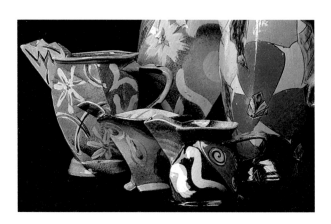

▷ Bowled Over's attractive handpainted earthenware pudding basins are produced in a wide range of patterns and six sizes. Any combination of pattern, name and size can be ordered and, for a small extra charge, printed with a name, date or message. Bowled Over also produce hand-thrown bowls, mugs, egg cups and jugs. For a leaflet, including prices and order form, send a stamped addressed envelope to *Bowled Over, Manor Farmhouse, Patney, Nr Devizes, Wilts. SN10 3RB. Tel.: 01380-840501.*

△ Love Unlimited is the workshop that Liz Riley set up in 1980 to create her own hand-built, hand-painted ceramics. Her decoration is a richly colourful celebration of fruit, flowers and animals. In the tableware illustrated, it is vibrant sunflowers on a green background. Prices range from £10 for the mug to £95 for the large plate; a wider choice is available. Contact *Love Unlimited Ceramics, 39 South St, Bedminster, Bristol BS3 3AU. Tel.: 0117-9660766.*

CERAMICS

▽ Lindy Brockway designs a remarkable selection of stunning hand-thrown and painted pottery, from platters, bowls, lidded jars, candlesticks, mugs and jugs to extravagant teapots, bread crocks, cache pots, cheese bells and lamps. A multitude of different shapes and sizes is available, although Lindy is also happy to accept individual orders. For example, she will design a complete dinner service to commission, or simply commemorate a special occasion with an elegant calligraphic monogram. She always uses top-quality clay, which does not chip and will last for years. Telephone Lindy to order, or make an appointment to visit her Fulham showroom, *Tel.: 0171-371 9739.*

◁ All the pots produced by John Jelfs's Cotswold Pottery are hand-thrown using traditional techniques, and glazed with the pottery's own glazes, made from local wood ash and clays. Each pot is therefore unique. This one is 45cm high and costs £95 (prices start at £20). Visit or contact the workshop, where a wide selection of pots is available, *Cotswold Pottery, Clapton Row, Bouton-on-the-Water, Glos. GL54 2DN. Tel.: 01451-820173.*

© Robin Brockway

▷ Anthony Parfitt's Kinetic Teapot would look at home alongside the gadgetry of a Batman film. Strikingly modern and set to become design classics, the teapots in this range owe their forms to the designer's background in architecture and his passion for sculpture, geometry and engineering. Handmade from metal and ceramic, they are functional as well as sculptural. For further information and mail order, contact *6 Springvale North, Dartford, Kent DA1 2LL. Tel.: 01322-287016.*

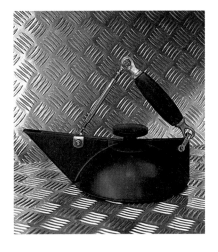

▽ This basket of fruit looks so appetizing and realistic that it is a surprise to discover that each piece is in fact ceramic. Lorraine Taylor and Nicky Smart of Penkridge Ceramics create an impressive collection of meticulously replicated fruits and vegetables, both common or garden and exotic. They make ten varieties of apple, pomegranates, quinces, parsnips and pumpkins, to name but a few (from £10 to £95). For a mail-order list, contact *Penkridge Ceramics, Argent Works, Bott Lane, Walsall, W. Mids WS1 2JJ. Tel.: 01922-25181.*

△ Items selected from the attractive Puffin Ware range from John O'Groats Pottery, which makes a wide variety of hand-thrown tableware, hand-built individual ceramics and slip-cast/modelled pieces. All are made from a porcelain/stoneware clay and decorated using various techniques, colours and glazes. For prices and order form, contact *John O'Groats Pottery, Unit 3, John O'Groats, Caithness KW1 4YR. Tel.: 01955-611284.*

◁ Maryse Boxer's innovative ceramic tableware, made in organic shapes and painted by hand, and her hand-blown glass are designed to be elements in table settings that can be combined with whatever china and glass you have already, to create a range of different moods. Together with textile designer Carolyn Quartermaine (see **Textiles**), Maryse blends the contemporary with the baroque to produce glamorous, avant-garde table settings. Prices range from £6 to £900. Visit their shop, *Maryse Boxer and Carolyn Quartermaine, Chez Joseph, 26 Sloane St, London SW1X 7LQ. Tel.: 0171-245 9493.*

△ This collection of colourful handmade bowls and plates is available from specialist shop Ceramica Blue (see also **Tiles**). Functional and highly decorative items from more than 20 potteries world-wide are for sale, but it is a wealth of vigorous pottery from Sicily that forms the heart of their stock. A wide range of tableware includes some pieces decorated with sun-drenched fruit and vegetables in Mediterranean colours, others with modern images in strong pastel tones. Many exceptional British potters are also represented. The pieces illustrated cost from £9 to £34. *Ceramica Blue, 10 Blenheim Cres., London W11 1NN. Tel.: 0171-727 0288.*

▷ Beguiling ceramic ornaments by Janice Wahnich and available by mail order from Covent Garden's eclectic emporium, Mildred Pearce. Perfect accessories for the bedroom or bathroom, the ceramic bottles in three speckled shades come with crocus or leaf stoppers and in two sizes: the tall bottles are £55, the short ones are £34. The leaf hand mirror costs £54; p & p is extra. *Mildred Pearce, 33 Earlham St, London WC2H 9LD. Tel.: 0171-379 5128.* See also **Clocks** and **Decorative Accessories.**

▽ Pretty pastel demi-tasse coffee cups, decorated with gold stars, from Jane Temple's range of hand-painted tableware. Bathroom accessories, lamps and her tableware are also available in a black and white rococo musical design, a bugs and butterflies design, a double-colour check pattern, and in spots and stripes. Jane's lamps can be hand-painted to match clients'

fabric; she also supplies card lampshades. A coffee cup and saucer costs £9.50. For a brochure, contact *Jane Temple Lamps & China, Reaside Farm, Neen Savage, Cleobury Mortimer, Kidderminster, Worcs. DY14 8ES. Tel.: 01299-271393.*

▽ Genevieve Neilson makes all her work by hand, decorating it with underglaze stains and oxides, using a wax-resist medium to build the designs. These are inspired by impressionist paintings, textiles and flowers. Initially working with inlay and applying wax resist to mask areas on her large dishes and vases, Genevieve adapted her technique to work on thrown pieces, so her range is more extensive. It is all dishwasher-safe. Prices range from £8 to £50, and she works to commission. Visit her shop or telephone Genevieve at *The Gallery, 13 Victoria St, Englefield Green, Surrey TW20 0QY. Tel.: 01784-430516.*

△ The barnyard inspired Paul Pigram to design this charming range of stencilled plant pots, suitable for indoor or outdoor use. The pots are painted in two coats of emulsion before being stencilled by hand in three colours, and then varnished to make them waterproof. The stencils are all individually cut by hand from Paul and Maxine Pigram's own designs. The pots are available in three sizes (10, 12 and 16cm), costing £6.95, £10.95 and £13.95 including p & p, by mail order from *Country Matters, Unit 1, Albert Mill, Compstall, Stockport, Cheshire SK6 5HN. Tel.: 0161-427 8085.*

▽ Developed through Hazle's love of the British High Street, these miniature pieces of nostalgia are cast from hand-carved models of real buildings. Every plaque is hand-painted and hand-dip glazed, with at least three kiln firings. With a painter's mark and the signature of the creator on each, this is a

remarkable series of collectables. Most of the buildings can be personalized to represent any shop you wish. Prices range from £29 to £45 (extra for personalizing). For stockists, contact *Hazle Ceramics, Stallions Yard, Codham Hall, Great Warley, Brentwood, Essex CM13 3JT. Tel.: 01277-220892.*

▽ These pretty hand-painted Tile Motifs will instantly transform plain tiles. Easy to fix with acrylic water-resistant tabs on the back, they can be used on any tile, coloured or white, hand- or factory-made. Designed to fit within a 10cm tile, they look equally good on larger tiles or other surfaces such as walls, mirrors and painted furniture. The range includes sea creatures, animals, fruit and nursery motifs. They cost £5.50 each + p & p and are available by mail order from *Crystal Palace Pottery, PO Box 4259, London SE26 6TG. Tel.: 0171-761 9490.*

◁ A series of designs combining themes of time (Roman numerals) and motion (cartographic images) adorn Julie Arnall's white crackle-glaze tiles, hand-painted with a gold or platinum lustre. Individual tiles can be placed at random or grouped to form original combinations. Panels are also available in a variety of sizes. Tiles cost from £14 each. Contact *Julie Arnall, 26 Woodwaye, Watford, Herts. WD1 4NW. Tel.: 01923-228465.* See also **Decorative Fixtures**.

▷ Inspired by 17th and 18thC Dutch tiles, Whichford Pottery have created an attractive range, hand-painted in the 'Delft' manner. As on the original tiles, tin glaze is applied to give them a soft, silk finish. Each tile is 12.5cm sq. and is available in cobalt or manganese. Whichford also stock their own range of contemporary designs in polychrome colours, including highly decorative tile panels. Prices start at £2.95 each for plain tiles with corner decorations, rising to £5.95 each for picture tiles. For a brochure, contact *Whichford Pottery, Whichford, Nr Shipston-on-Stour, War. CV36 5PG. Tel.: 01608-684416,* quoting 'Delft' tiles.

△ A small selection of hand-decorated feature and border tiles from Kenneth Clark Ceramics' broad range of highly individual designs. They also produce hand-sprayed plain coloured tiles, repeat designs and ceramic panels and murals. When working to commission, they tailor tile schemes to the needs of individual customers. Decorative techniques include hand-painting, stencilling and tubelining. For prices and catalogue, contact *Kenneth Clark Ceramics, The North Wing, Southover Grange, Southover Rd, Lewes, E. Sussex BN7 1TP. Tel.: 01273-476761.*

TILES

▷ Specialists in tile decoration of all kinds – printing, painting and stencilling – on their own handmade or on commercially produced tiles, Clays sell a range of over 40 decorative tiles, of which the strawberry trellis border, illustrated, was the first. Prices start at £6.50 for a decorated tile, £45 per sq. yd + VAT for plain tiles. They also sell wall plaques and accept commissions. *Clays Handmade Tiles, 110 Leavesden Rd, Watford, Herts. WD2 5EG. Tel.: 01923-240094.*

◁ A collection of vibrant, highly coloured decorative tiles available from Ceramica Blue, the shop that specializes in handmade, hand-painted ceramics (see also **Ceramics** p. 64). Reflecting a wide spectrum of modern designs and decoration, their stock includes the work of individual British ceramicists, family-run studios in Italy, and from countries as far-flung as South Africa. The tiles illustrated cost from £5.50 to £9. Visit the shop or telephone for further details: *Ceramica Blue, 10 Blenheim Cres., London W11 1NN. Tel.: 0171-727 0288.*

▷ These pretty handmade tiles by potter Mark de la Torre have a fossil-like appearance, created by pressing leaves into the tiles before they are fired. Shown in aquamarine and cobalt blue, they also come in mustard and with a variety of leaf imprints. They measure 4in. sq. (10cm sq.) and cost £4 each + p & p. *De La Torre Tiles, The Courtyard, The Old Rectory, Stoke Lacy, Hereford HR7 4HH. Tel.: 01432-820500.*

▷ Stunning glazed tiles in lovely muted colours form Fired Earth's Studio Tile range, which focuses on traditional smallscale production from England and France. These tiles are handmade in the Alps, and cost £2.53 each. Fired Earth supply high-quality tiles in plain or decorative finishes from all over the world. Contact *Fired Earth, Twyford Mill, Oxford Rd, Adderbury, Oxon OX17 3HP. Tel.: 01295-812088.* (See also **Flooring** and **Wallpaper and Paint**)

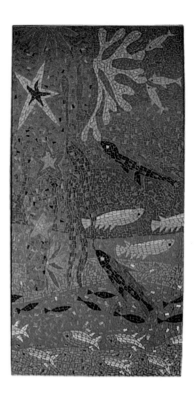

▷ The glorious colours in this glass mosaic panel seem luminescent. It is by Mosaic Workshop, who design and make mosaics to commission in glass, marble, smalti and unglazed ceramic. Commissions include floors, walls, signs and features for swimming pools. They also restore existing mosaics, produce a range of mosaic objects – mirrors, tiles, furniture and jewellery – and have recently brought out an attractive mosaic kit based on a Roman design. For prices and more details, contact *Mosaic Workshop, Unit B, 443-449 Holloway Rd, London N7 6LJ. Tel.: 0171-263 2997.*

△ Danka Napiorkowska is a designer of unique decorated tile panels for kitchens and bathrooms, such as this Miro lady, and tile murals for swimming pools and jacuzzis. She uses beautiful on-glaze enamel colours to ensure a durable, colourful finish. Danka works to commission, offering a complete design service. She also has a cheaper 'off the peg' range of tiles from £8; panels from £100. Contact her at *Little Treforda, Trewalder, Delabole, Cornwall PL33 9EY. Tel.: 01208-812024.*

△ A stunning Flamingo glass mosaic, 66cm in diameter, by Martin Cheek, who has made mosaic animals something of a speciality. A gecko, stag beetle and gold-crested crane number among his subjects. He uses a variety of materials including glass, smalti and raku-fired ceramic tesserae. Martin teaches at the Royal College of Art, has had many successful exhibitions, and runs mosaic and ceramic courses in Broadstairs. The Flamingo mosaic costs £495. For further information, contact *Martin Cheek, 53 Pursers Cross Rd, London SW6 4QY. Tel.: 0171-731 0241.*

Glass

Blown, blasted, polished, cut, etched or stained, this section covers the spectrum of uses, both practical and decorative, for this versatile material.

▷ An assembled bowl in moulded recycled glass, with sections linked by thread-bound wire. Also available: assembled glass baskets, glass tiles, mirrors, wall hangings and jewellery. Jewellery starts at £15; baskets at £80. Commissions welcome. Contact *Heidi Westgate, Unit 3a, The Star Brewery, Castle Ditch Lane, Lewes, E. Sussex BN7 1YJ. Tel.: 01273-486356.*

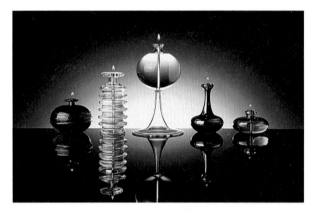

△ Exotic yet functional, these hand-blown oil lamps are part of a wide range of pieces by Sue Keelan. She also makes scent bottles, wrought-iron table pieces that incorporate oil lamps, chandeliers, wall sconces, jewellery with unique blown-glass beads, and interesting Christmas decorations. Prices start at £10, available from *Sue Keelan Glass, The Stables, Cargill, Perth PH2 6DS. Tel.: 01250-883365.*

△ Quirky and distinctive, these items from the Coloured Ball range are handmade from recycled glass. Bob Crooks adds the colour by rolling the hot glass over small chips of coloured glass. Each piece is individually handblown and hand-finished, making it distinct from any other. Bob manufactures a variety of ranges, as well as limited editions and scent bottles. He welcomes commissions. Prices range from £10 to £1,000 per item, from *First Glass, Unit 2a, Union Court, Union Rd, London SW4 6JP. Tel.: 0171-622 3322.*

◁ An elegant water sculpture in plate glass and stainless steel. Its identical glass pieces, which fan out gradually, allow for great variety in shape and size. Specializing in architectural and sculptural commissions, this company makes smaller pieces starting at £1,500. Contact *Peter Layton Associates, 7 The Leather Market, Weston St, London SE1 3ER. Tel.: 0171-403 2800.*

▽ Ann Wood makes sculptural and decorative pieces, such as this striking Stack Candlestick. A stack of fused glass supports a cup hand-painted with enamel. This versatile artist focuses on traditional kiln-firing techniques, drawing upon her love of ancient civilizations for inspiration. She has fulfilled commissions for clients all over the world, including private individuals, interior designers, fashion designers, architects and private galleries. As well as maintaining tried-and-tested ranges, Ann also spends time developing new ranges of glass vessels, candlesticks, clocks, lights, mirrors and jewellery. Her candlesticks start at £26. For further information, contact *Ann Wood Glass, Unit 15, The Metropolitan Workshops, Enfield Rd, London N1 5AZ. Tel.: 0181-340 0956.*

△ A stunning leaded window in handblown and machine-antiqued glass, with bevelled glass squares. Beverly Bryon employs traditional methods such as painting, acid-etching, silver-staining and sand-blasting to produce fine stained-glass windows in abstract and stylized linear design. This window is 8.7 sq. m (29 sq. ft) and was made in 13 sections. Beverly also creates screens, lights, mirrors, doors, skylights and hanging panels – for interior designers, architects and private individuals. She encourages a client's involvement in the design process, can reproduce any period style, and provides a restoration service. Prices range from £70 per sq. ft (30 sq. cm) to £170 per sq. ft. *Prisms Stained Glass Design, Unit 31, Kingsgate Workshops, 114 Kingsgate Rd, London NW6 2JG. Tel.: 0171-624 3240.*

▷ This fluid, small 'wavy rim' bowl is painstakingly made by hand. It is blown with thin layers of colour added while hot and then it is sand-blasted. The decoration is cut into the glass and the bowl is fire-polished. It costs about £280. Other 'wavy rim' designs are available, also ranges of wine glasses, jugs and candlesticks. Commissions welcome. Contact *Deborah Fladgate, Fladgate Glass Studio, Greenside House, Leslie, Fife KY6 3DF. Tel.: 01592-741355.*

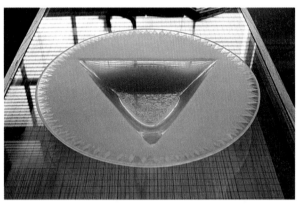

△ Acid-etching and sand-blasting techniques have contributed to the design and texture of this attractive platter by Jane Cole. She uses recycled glass, sometimes further decorated with gold, silver and copper, to make bowls, plates and platters. Jewellery is also available. Prices start at £10 for a small bowl; from *Glassworks, 39 Trafalgar St, Brighton BN1 4ED. Tel.: 01273-686542.*

▽ Made from freeblown recycled lead glass, this posy vase and bottle illustrate Jane Charles's imaginative work. Each of her pieces is unique and she welcomes commissions. Prices start at £30, from *Jane Charles Studio Glass, Units 19 and 20, Premier Workshops, Whitehouse Rd, Scotswood, Newcastle upon Tyne, NE15 6EP. Tel: 0191-228 0152.*

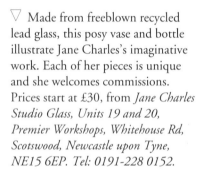

◁ A once-secret casting technique has helped to create this fine small bowl. Granulated glass is ground by hand with a binding agent to form a paste, which is applied inside a mould and fused in a kiln. Emma Wood and Keith Crome produce delicate and experimental pieces. Prices start at £28, from *Glassworks, 39 Trafalgar St, Brighton BN1 4ED. Tel.: 01273-686542.*

▷ Ancient symbolism, tapestries, tiles and architecture have inspired the timeless and expressive design of Gaynor Ringland's textural bowls. They are fired twice in a kiln, first to fuse the enamels and then to shape the glass. The vibrant enamels provide a base for the scratchy patterning, and each piece is unique. Gaynor also makes earrings, brooches and accessories. Prices start at £24, from *Gaynor Ringland, 2 The Grove, Portway, Warminster, Wilts. BA12 8QL. Tel.: 01985-216187.*

◁ This picturesque and detailed scene of a Pyrenean mountain village is set in a nearby farmhouse that has been converted by a retired English couple. The window has been made using traditional methods, from handmade glass and lead cames. Glass Heritage Ltd can produce stained-glass in a wide range of designs for windows, doors and ceilings, taking into account the architecture and interior of a house, and a client's tastes. They specialize in commissions for private individuals, offering a free design service, and will also install anywhere in the UK or abroad. Visitors to the studio and showroom are welcome. Prices start at £200 for a small door panel, available from *Gerald Paxton, Glass Heritage Ltd, Reynolds Warehouse, The Docks, Glos. GL1 2EN. Tel.: 01452-503803.*

GLASS

▽ David Weeks makes his glassware from recycled lead crystal, which he blows by mouth and finishes by hand. These Aqua bowls cost £28, and the vases £22. Most of David's designs are functional and modern, and he uses colour to delicate effect. An experienced glass designer, he welcomes commissions. *David Weeks, The Glassblowers Workshop, The Star Brewery, Castle Ditch Lane, Lewes, E. Sussex BN7 1YJ. Tel.: 01273-486356.*

◁ This vibrant and eye-catching mirror is created by Georgina Lester, who designs and makes an enormous variety of pieces. She uses glass to produce anything from vases, candle-holders and mirrors to stained-glass windows, window hangings and screens, including jewellery and *objets d'art*. She is currently assembling a collection of one-off pieces for sale. *Georgina Lester, The Workhouse, Hatherleigh Place, Union Rd, Abergavenny, Gwent NP7 9SA. Tel.: 01873-831501.*

▷ These exquisite, delicately designed, freeblown glass vases in the Blossom Series reflect the innovative style, colour and texture of handmade pieces by the sister company of Peter Layton Associates (see p. 70). They welcome commissions; prices start at £15, from *The London Glassblowing Workshop, 7 The Leather Market, Weston St, London SE1 3ER. Tel.: 0171-403 2800.*

△ The aptly named Dimple range by Hothouse is made entirely by hand. Classical in theme and tactile, it is only one example of this company's work. Set up in 1987, Hothouse produces handmade pieces ranging from small perfume bottles and paperweights to lampshades and large items. Prices £19.50-£250. *Hothouse, 7 Lumsdale Mill, Lower Lumsdale, Matlock, Derbs. DE4 5EX. Tel.: 01629-580821.*

△ Delicate in design and rich in colour, this stained-glass fanlight is made from handblown glass and costs £850. Kate Baden Fuller also creates door panels, stairwell windows, screens and room dividers, with each design individually tailored to a client's needs. Contact *Kate Baden Fuller, 90 Greenwood Rd, London E8 1NE. Tel.: 0171-249 0858.*

▽ Reminiscent of Lalique and monumental in scale, this pair of doors measures 3 x 2.5m. The luminescent glass panels are hand-cast from glass acrylic, and the surface is treated to suggest ancient pieces retrieved from the bottom of the sea. The door frame is made from wood, clad with pewter. Nick Allen works to both private and public commissions to design and handmake glass that is extraordinary and unique. His speciality is exploring themes and techniques and his broad range includes glass door handles, screens, lighting, signs, furniture and glassware. *Nick Allen, Glass Workshops, 1-3 Shelgate Rd, London SW11 1BD. Tel.: 0171-738 0050.*

▷ Traditional freeblown skills, combined with gold- and silver-leaf decoration, have produced these jewel-like perfume bottles. Joy and Darrell Greenhalgh also handmake a wide range of bowls, vessels and one-off pieces, starting at £48.50. Contact *Greenhalgh Glass, The Glassblowing Workshop, Caudwell's Mill, Derbs. DE4 2EB. Tel.: 01773-520671.*

▽ Inspired by the Roman era, these handblown engraved bowls are made from lead crystal – as decorative as it is functional. Lisa Cross's designs range from candlesticks and perfume bottles to larger vases and dishes. The bowls shown here cost £40. Contact *Lisa Cross, 81a Filsham Rd, St Leonard's-on-Sea, E. Sussex TN38 0PE. Tel.: 01585-709973.*

△ Individually produced from fine coloured crystal decorated in a unique process, these vibrant bowls are part of a co-ordinating range that includes perfume bottles and goblets. The Batik range is handmade by Bev Jacks and her partner, Iestyn Davies. Prices start at £30, from *Blowzone Glass Studio, Platts Rd, Amblecote, Stourbridge, W. Midlands DY8 4YR. Tel.: 01384-444654.*

◁ Sesame and Lillies specialize in period-style, hand-painted decorative glass panels, designed and made to order, and to fit doors, hallways, windows and partitioning. This art nouveau example has been made with raised leadwork. They make an extensive range to private and commercial commissions. Price range: £150 per sq. m to £450 per sq. m. Contact *Katrina Walker-Hamlett, Sesame and Lillies, The Tower, Woodhill, Kinellar, Aberdeen AB2 0RZ. Tel.: 01224-791441.*

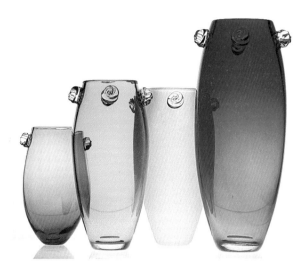

△ Classic shapes and a rainbow of colours distinguish this Twist range of mouthblown crystal (small sample illustrated). Rich reds, blues, greens and yellows combine to decorate a graceful collection of tumblers, jugs, vases, decanters, perfume bottles and bowls. Prices start at £16.38. Other collections are available, as well as mirrors and tables, from *Tinsley Davies Design, 134 Shoreditch High St, London E1 6JE. Tel.: 0171-729 6322.*

▽ Masterfully combining ancient and contemporary influences, this handmade glassware is decorated with precious metals, which are melted into the glass while it is still hot. The pieces shown here cost £34.50-£195. Adam Aaronson also handmakes door and cupboard handles, paperweights, vases, bowls, candlesticks and tableware. His showroom is at *The Handmade Glass Co. Ltd, Studio S, The Old Imperial Laundry, 71 Warriner Gardens, London SW11 4XW. Tel.: 0171-627 5555.*

△ Fun and boldly decorated, these glasses form part of a range of hand-painted enamelled glassware. Each piece is individually painted, then etched to reveal the original glass surface. The range includes glasses, vases, bowls, jugs and coffee mugs. Commissions are welcome. Prices range from £18 to £150. Contact *Mark Prest Glass, Manchester Craft Centre, 17 Oak St, Manchester M4 5JB. Tel.: 0161-832 4274.*

△ Millennium Tableware specialize in exclusive collections made from mouthblown glass, fine china, stoneware, ironstone and other ceramics. These shimmering lustre glasses, starting at £2.95 for a wine glass, form the St. James Festival Collection, and complement tableware of the same name in fine china. Other glass designs include barleytwist candle-holders, stoppered decanters and vinaigrette bottles. Contact *Millennium Tableware Ltd, 7 Swallow Place, London W1R 7AD. Tel.: 0171-493 3313.* See also **Ceramics**.

Beverly Beeland, *401½ Workshops, 401½, Wandsworth Rd, London SW8 2JP (Tel.: 0171-498 7045)*, works in a number of mediums as well as glass, including etched metals, carved wood and ceramics.

Bridgewater Glass, *739 Fulham Rd, London SW6 5UL (Tel.: 0171-371 9033)* produces pretty handmade decorated glass, which is designed by Emma Bridgewater and harks back to the 19thC.

Martin Donlin *(Tel.: 01202-739063)* works to commission, specializing in large pieces – acid-etched and polished windows, screens and glass blocks – as well as stained glass.

Ruth Dresman Glass, *The Meads, West Knoyle, Warminster, Wilts. BA12 6AE (Tel.: 01747-830085)*, produces beautifully decorated pieces in subtle colours.

The Glasshouse, *21 St. Albans Pl., Islington, London N1 0NX (Tel.: 0171-359 8162)*, is a gallery and showcase for a number of talented designers, whose work is both quirky and attractive.

MAP, *165a Junction Rd, London N19 5PZ (Tel.: 0171-263 8529)*, decorate and transfer glass and china with designs that range from sea creatures to fortune symbols.

Rimmington Vian, *5a Iliffe Yard, Crampton St, London SE17 3QA (Tel.: 0171-708 0864)*, produce a collection of stunning handmade glass tableware decorated with enamel or gold.

Shakspeare Glassworks, *Riverside Pl., Taunton, Somerset TA1 1JJ (Tel.: 01823-333422)*, make a range of glass pieces by hand with pleasing shapes and swirling abstract designs.

Silver

Prized for its lustre and malleability, silver has attracted craftsmen and collectors alike for thousands of years. Bowls, beakers, tea and coffee pots, candlesticks and egg cups... 20thC silversmiths are making these and more besides.

▽ 'Have nothing in your house that you do not know to be useful and believe to be beautiful.' The words were William Morris's, but silversmith Patricia Hamilton shares the sentiment. Her pieces are simple, elegant and sculptural: see, for example, the beautiful lines of her cutlery. Her range includes jugs, bowls and salt cellars (many of silver with gilt inside), candlesticks, vases, coffee pots and teapots, butter knives, caddy spoons and teaspoons. Patricia also specializes in anodized aluminium pieces in rich, striking colours, such as these plates. For prices and further information, contact *Patricia Hamilton, The Mill, Hardwick, Witney, Oxon OX8 7QE. Tel.: 01865-300407.*

◁ Characteristic of the work of talented silversmith Howard Fenn are the bold clear lines and sculptural qualities demonstrated by the candlesticks and vase illustrated. Other designs combine silver with another material such as slate. His ebony hairbrushes with silver inlay are much sought after. Howard accepts commissions and produces one-off experimental pieces, which challenge the dividing line between art and craft. Prices start at £75. *Howard Fenn, 9 The Leathermarket, Weston St, London SE1 3ER. Tel.: 0171-378 9222.*

△ Part of Richardson & Ottewill's exclusive range of tableware, these elegant silver/gilt goblets have been carefully created to be functional as well as aesthetically pleasing. The aventurine stone serves as an excellent focal point for the goblet, from which the curved lines seem to 'grow' (£470 each or £940 a pair). Richardson & Ottewill work to commission, making one-off pieces and production runs in gold and silver. *Richardson & Ottewill, Evegate, Station Rd, Smeeth, Ashford, Kent TN25 6SX. Tel.: 01303-814484.*

▽ For a special present to celebrate a wedding, anniversary or christening, Count Your Blessings have brought out a range of smart sterling silver gifts. Each item has the date of the occasion cut out in Roman numerals. The collection includes coasters, cufflinks, earrings, brooches and the napkin rings shown below, which cost £80 each (£92 if gold-plated). For a brochure, contact *Count Your Blessings, 78b Ashley Gdns, Thirleby Rd, London SW1P 1HG. Tel.: 0171-931 7425.*

▷ Annie Boursot started her business six years ago with the aim of providing affordable modern and antique silver and plate. This silver-plated rose bowl is one of many well-designed items, perfect for gifts and available by mail order. Other services include a search and find for antique silver, engraving, repairs, wedding lists and commissions. Boursot's modern silver range is always growing with Annie's own designs. For a catalogue, telephone *Boursot, Tel.: 01488-668628/Fax.: 01488-668853.*

△ Claire Underwood's stunning silver egg cups (£175) and spoons (£119), decorated with brightly coloured enamel, are part of a range that includes functional pieces like these, plus napkin rings and paper knives, and more decorative pieces, such as jewellery, pill boxes and perfume bottles. Red, yellow, green and blue predominate, reflecting the influence that living in Africa has had on Claire's work: the colours are those used in African fabrics and beadwork. Contact her at *Studio W6, Cockpit Workshops, Northington St, London WC1N 2NP. Tel.: 0171-916 9013.*

SILVER

The four remarkable designs illustrated on this page are the work of renowned Irish silversmith Kevin O'Dwyer. His beautiful hand-crafted jewellery, tableware, teapots and candlesticks are dramatic in design, blurring the boundaries between function, fashion and pure sculpture. Internationally, O'Dwyer's reputation gathers increasing momentum. Recipients of his work include President Nelson Mandela, King Juan Carlos of Spain and former French President François Mitterrand. His jewellery costs from £50, candlesticks from £500, teapots and coffee services from £3,000. Available from *Artizana, The Village, Prestbury, Cheshire SK10 4DG. Tel.: 01625-827582.* Artizana also specializes in glass, ceramics, woodwork, textiles and paintings, and has a furniture gallery (see **Tables and Chairs** and **Small Furniture**).

△ Beautiful sterling silver salt and matching pepper pots, whose design is both sculptural and tactile.

▽ The dramatic quality of Kevin O'Dwyer's work is particularly evident in his architectural coffee service in sterling silver.

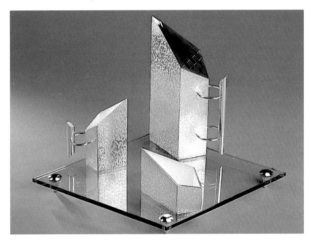

▽ Simple and elegant, these candlesticks are among Kevin O'Dwyer's most delicate pieces.

▽ A stunning rocking teapot, made from green patinated bronze and gold-plated silver.

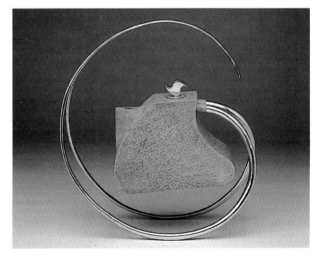

▽ Ingenious use of gold, silver, pearls and precious stones has made John Donald a designer of international repute, whose creations are brought to life by his own workshop of skilled craftsmen. The only remaining goldsmith in the City of London, John Donald has occupied the same premises in Cheapside – street of the leading goldsmiths since the 13thC – for the past 23 years. He will design to order ceremonial regalia, presentation silverware, elegant centrepieces and beautiful jewellery. Estimates and designs to model stage are offered free of charge. For the pieces illustrated, prices range from £99 for the butter knife to £916 for the nugget-edge silver tray (30cm in diameter). Contact *John Donald, 120 Cheapside, London EC2V 6DR. Tel.: 0171-606 2675.*

◁ Somerset designer/silversmith Caroline Lytton decorates her hand-raised or forged silverware with unique designs, chased in low relief or contrasting texture. She makes mostly one-off pieces including beakers, bowls, christening cups and unusual spoons. As this Orchid beaker illustrates, her designs are often inspired by plants, as well as animals, fossils and architectural motifs. Prices start at £40 for caddy spoons and £450 for beakers. Contact *Caroline Lytton, Tel.: 01643-705797.*

SILVER

▽ Frances Julie Whitelaw's solid silver quaichs have exquisitely simple lines. They stand on small ebony bases and are loosely derived from the traditional Scottish whisky drinking vessels. They are 8cm in diameter and cost from £250 each. Frances Julie also makes spoons (from £50), which are popular christening presents, individual or sets of napkin rings and teapots, all to commission. Contact *Frances Julie Whitelaw, Cleveland Crafts Centre, 57 Gilkes St, Middlesbrough, Cleveland TS1 5EL. Tel.: 01642-226351.*

◁ Third-generation silversmith Anton Pruden shares a workshop with Rebecca Smith in Ditchling, where Anton's grandfather was silversmith. Numerous commissions include a lectern for Liverpool's Metropolitan Cathedral. They also make practical items, such as these salad servers in solid silver with sealed hardwood handles (£150, or £180 with the bowl). Their wide range can be seen at their workshop or supplied by mail order. *Anton Pruden & Rebecca Smith, Turner Dumbrell Workshops, North End, Ditchling, E. Sussex BN6 8TD. Tel.: 01273-846338.*

▷ This silver coffee set is typical of Keith Redfern's current designs in both style and character: classic simple forms balanced by contrasting linear rhythms. All pieces, large and small, are individually designed, hand-wrought and made to order. His work is held in many important collections, for example, H.M. The Queen, H.M. The Queen Mother and City Livery Companies. Recent works include a flagon for Lichfield Cathedral and water jugs and a cigar box for 10 Downing Street, commissioned by the Silver Trust. Prices £200-5,000. Contact *Keith Redfern Designs, Tel./Fax.: 0181-788 0398; or c/o Goldsmiths' Company, Foster Lane, London EC2V 6BN.*

△ These salt dishes and spoons are typical of Philippa Merriman's silver style – simple, clear and balanced. Each piece, whether raised, forged or fabricated, looks and feels uncluttered and complete. Most of her work is tableware but she also makes presentation pieces and jewellery to order. While working mainly in sterling silver, in some pieces she incorporates gold and woods such as ebony and walnut. Contact *Philippa Merriman, Westfield House, West Rd, Lancaster LA1 5PE. Tel.: 01524-382323.*

▽ Chris Knight's silver/gilt water pitchers are elements in a range of tableware including teapots and vessels in precious and non-precious metals. Through the use of computer-aided design and traditional silversmithing techniques, he strives to create a tension between the visual and the functional. He designs one-off and limited-edition pieces to commission (commissions start at £500). *Chris Knight, 101 Hambalt Rd, Clapham Common, London SW4 9EL. Tel.: 0181-673 2017.*

△ Keith Tyssen prefers 'a design that makes a bold visual statement, but calmly so', believing that an object should have a 'reassuring presence, enabling it to stand alone, yet also able to harmonise within its setting'. His modern pewter centrepiece – a clever combination of flared pot vessel (14cm high), 20cm dish and 30cm bowl, all of which can be used independently – and bowl (17.5cm) fulfill his criteria perfectly. These designs use a double-skin hollow construction to achieve visual weight and some thermal insulation, are resistant to tarnishing and have a satin finish. Among other designs in pewter and silver are candlesticks, biscuit barrels, vases and belt buckles. For further details, contact *Keith Tyssen, 80 Gell St, Sheffield S3 7QW. Tel.: 0114-273 0639.*

▽ Richard Fox established his present company, designing and making his own silverware in 1993. Much of his work is to commission; pieces include chalices, trophies, medals and cruet sets. Among his stock items are candlesticks, ice buckets, cocktail shakers, pens and pieces of exclusive tableware – his latest range is illustrated below. In both aspects of his work, he achieves simple, elegant, tactile designs. Prices for stock items range from £25 to £7,050. Richard has exhibited widely throughout Britain, Europe and America. He also designs original jewellery. For further details, contact *Richard Fox & Associates, 9a Peacock Yard, Iliffe St, London SE17 3LH. Tel.: 0171-701 5540.*

△ Beautiful hand-raised pieces in silver, chased in low relief with inlaid fine gold details, are Rod Kelly's speciality. The chased images often depict plants and flowers. These pepper grinders and salts were commissioned by Green College,

Oxford. Other commissions include pieces for H.M. The Queen Mother and No. 10 Downing Street. Rod's designs range from a napkin ring to a centrepiece. Prices start at £250. Contact him *c/o Goldsmiths' Company, Foster Lane, London, EC2V 6BN,* or on *Tel.: 01953-717625.*

▽ Malcolm Appleby started his career as an engraver and currently designs for a silver and specialist gun engraver. He has developed new techniques, fusing gold on to steel and for engraving silver.Commissions have included the 500th anniversary silver cup for the London Assay Office, a V & A seal, a condiment set for 10 Downing Street, and engraving the orb on the Prince of Wales Coronet. His work is to be found in collections throughout the world from Scotland to South Australia. This attractive silver bowl is beaded with 22ct gold beads and is one of a number of similar designs of different sizes. For prices and further information, contact *Malcolm Appleby, Crathes Station, Banchory, Kincardineshire AB3 3JE. Tel.: 01330-844642.*

▷ The interrelationship of different forms and materials is central to the work of Simone ten Hompel. She frequently combines steel with silver, emphasizing the contrast between the two very different metals. Basing her choice of material on its practical and visual nature, she also combines metals with wood, and silver with gold plate, as in the salt and pepper pots illustrated. For further details, contact Simone at *14 Clerkenwell Green, London EC1R 0DP. Tel.: 0171-490 3092.*

Textiles

*Warp and weft provide the texture, and the skills of the
dyer, printer and painter add the colour, beauty and
originality to a myriad of textiles.*

△ Building on many years' experience as an antique dealer, Belinda Coote has become a leading expert in fine reproduction French tapestries. Her collection represents all manner of patterns, weaves, sizes and periods, ranging from wall-hangings, fabrics and simple decorative borders to cushions, paisley throws and fabric-covered furniture. An extensive mail-order catalogue is available by post, for £2 including p & p, and her prices start at £20, rising to £3,000. Alternatively, her range can be viewed at *Belinda Coote, 29 Holland St, London W8 4NA. Tel.: 0171-937 3924;* or at her new extended area on the *4th Floor, Harvey Nichols, Knightsbridge, London SW1X 7RJ. Tel.: 0171-235 5000.*

▷ The White Company sells anything from crisp bed linen in 100% cotton and antique-effect embroidered bedspreads to goose-down duvets and simple china – most of it in white and all available by mail order only. Prices range from £2.50 for a coffee mug to £150 for a super-kingsize duvet. For more information about their enormous range, contact *The White Company, 298-300 Munster Rd, London SW6 6BH. Tel.: 0171-385 7988.*

▽ Woven by hand in 100% cotton, the bed- and tablelinen from Turquaz come in an extensive range of about 30 designs in checks, stripes and plaids. Their single duvet covers start at £48 and pillowcases with button fastenings at £12. *Turquaz, The Coach House, Bakery Pl., 119 Altenburg Gdns, London SW11 1JQ. Tel.: 0171-924 6894.*

△ Attractive bedlinen, in 100% cotton and detailed with traditional linen button fastenings, is available by mail order from Old Town. They offer five different gingham designs, three tartans and five chambrays, with duvet covers in single, double and kingsize, priced at £39, £49 and £59 respectively; and pillowcases costing £10.95 each. (Add £2.50 p & p to all orders.) *Old Town, 32 Elm Hill, Norwich NR3 1HG. Tel.: 01603-628100.*

◁ Virtually indistinguishable from the antique originals upon which they are based, replicas of Edwardian and Victorian bedlinens in cotton and linen are made by Antique Designs. Most are handworked with crochet, embroidery and drawnthread. A variety of pillowcases, pillowshams, sheets, duvet covers and accessories are made, with prices ranging from £4 to £200. For a list of retailers or mail-order details, contact *Antique Designs, 4 Stretton Hall Mews, Hall La., Lower Stretton, Cheshire WA4 4NY. Tel.: 01925-730909.*

▷ Handmade from both antique and contemporary fabrics, old lace and 1930s and '50s buttons, these items are produced by Pauline Bayne. The themes and picture effects on her pillows, potpourri sachets, cushion covers, wall hangings and quilted throws are achieved by clever combinations of colour, texture and dimension, with each item being individually and thoughtfully designed. Prices range from £5 to £200. *Pauline Bayne, Tel.: 0181-940 8261.*

▽ Luxurious square pillows filled with goose feather or a mixture of goose feather and down are supplied by mail order from Miller & Schültz. Also pillowcases in plain white, with button fastenings and scalloped or embroidered edges. All bedlinen is made from 100% cotton in white or blue-and-white checks, with pillows starting at £19.50; pillowcases at £6.50; and duvet covers at £19.95. (Pure down duvets are made to order.) *Miller & Schültz, South Kenwood, Kenton, Exeter EX6 8EX. Tel.: 01626-891672.*

△ Soft, comfortable knitted cushions, crafted by hand in 100% wool – a mixture of lambswool, Shetland and Donegal tweed, and in muted antique shades, in either a tartan or floral design. The larger cushion measures 18in. (45cm), costing £45; the smaller measures 14in. (35cm) and costs £42. (Prices include a feather-filled pad.) Blankets are also supplied, in a riot of knitted patchwork pieces, hand-worked in the same wools as the cushions. For further details, contact *Alison Dupernex, 19 Britannia Sq., Worcester WR1 3DG. Tel.: 01905-726937.*

◁ Hand-stitched quilts, luxurious bedspreads and crisp, pure cotton and linen can all be found at The Language of Flowers. Inspired by all things floral, a selection of bedlinen contains classic antique pieces and traditional sheets, as well as more contemporary throws and duvet covers. Delicate nightwear and handkerchieves are also available from the shop. Prices range from £22 to £420. *The Language of Flowers, 30 The Pantiles, Royal Tunbridge Wells, Kent TN2 5TN. Tel.: 01892-526090.*

▽ Flamboyant textiles by Zara Siddiqui, who hand-prints on to silk and suede, continually experimenting to create brilliant hues. Zara's collection of fabrics consists of over a hundred combinations and styles, which she uses for soft furnishings, upholstery and wall-hangings, or to make pictures set in gilt frames. Cushions start at £39.99; framed silks at £49.99; and footstools at £199.99. *Zara Siddiqui, Tel.: 0181-851 1471.*

△ Evocative of the Mediterranean and soft in texture, the cushions and floorcoverings by Zanna Rand-Bell are made from 100% linen, which she has dyed and woven by hand to produce simple checks, stripes and twills. For orders over £100, Zanna can dye the cloth specially for a customer, if required, so that it matches upholstery and so on. Prices start at £45 for an 18in. (45cm) cushion, including a feather pad. For further information, contact *Zanna Rand-Bell, 130 Fawe Pk Rd, London SW15 2EQ. Tel.: 0181-874 2503.*

▷ 'Chickens and Ticking' is one of a variety of cushions based on sketches drawn during Rachel Howard's travels in India. She uses a combination of screen-printing, appliquéd fabrics and machine embroidery, and also makes wall hangings. The cushions measure 18in. sq. (45cm) or 22in. sq. (55cm) and cost from £45 to £75. For more details, contact *Rachel Howard, 22 Thomas House, Morning La., London E9 6LB. Tel.: 0181-986 9889.*

▽ A Japanese textile designer, based in London, Hikaru Noguchi makes lively cushions, such as these 'ripple-patch' and 'woven-ribbon' versions, which start at £120. She applies similar textiles (velvets, ribbons and knitted fabrics) and techniques to footstools. *Hikaru Noguchi Textile Design, Unit W4, Cockpit Workshops, Cockpit Yd, Northington St, London WC1N 2NP. Tel.: 0171-916 3823.*

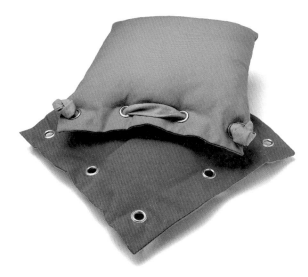

△ Beldecor Designs offer a complete soft-furnishing service, providing curtains, blinds, pelmets, upholstery, loose covers, napery, bed dressings, fabric walling and so on. Their eyelet cushions cost from £39 each, including the pad. *Beldecor Designs, 12 Royal Parade, Dawes Rd, London SW6 7RE. Tel.: 0171-381 5004.*

◁ Patchworked together from hand-printed fabrics, these cushions are hand-stitched and beaded by Lydia Bates, who also makes quilts, throws and drawstring bags. The cushions come in two sizes: 8in. (20cm) for £19.95 and 18in. (45cm) for £39.95, including a feather pad. There are eight animal designs to choose from, available by mail order. *Lydia Bates, 39 Queens Rd, Twickenham, Middx TW1 4EZ. Tel.: 0181-892 6579.*

▷ Textured, elegant and crisp, Alison Morton's collection of bathroom and kitchen towels are made from 100% cotton and/or linen, finely woven by hand, with bright dashes of colour added by way of decorative stripes. Hanging loops are woven into many of the designs and all the towels are machine-washable. Prices range from £14.85 for a facecloth to about £80 for a particularly luxurious bath towel + p & p. *Alison Morton, Eagles Yd, Machynlleth, Powys SY20 8AG. Tel.: 01654-703864.*

▽ Fiona Hills designs and makes wall-hangings to commission. She created this one, entitled 'The Miser', by screen-printing on to velvet brocade, and she usually works with cotton, silk and damask, applying decoration by printing and hand-painting. Although Fiona favours traditional themes, contemporary designs also appear in her work. Prices start at £850 for 10ft (3m) of fabric. *Fiona Hills, Tel.: 0171-603 2841/Fax: 0171-602 1779.*

△ Unique blends of embroidery and felt produce fashion accessories and soft furnishings, made from 100% wool in the Orkney Islands by Tait & Style. These Scottie cushions cost £60, measuring 57 sq. cm, and are available with matching throws. For more details on an innovative range of scarves, waistcoats, hats and so on, or made-to-order items, contact *Tait & Style, Brae Studio, Old Academy, Back Rd, Stromness, Orkney KW16 3AW. Tel.: 01856-851186.*

◁ Employing cotton chenille, Maia Diver makes a selection of hand-woven and hand-dyed runners, as illustrated. Measuring 38 x 150cm, they cost £75-80. Maia also creates hand-woven cushions in a similar style, as well as larger throws and wall hangings. *Maia Diver, 49 Gilpin Cresc., Twickenham, Middx TW2 7BP. Tel.: 0181-898 7421.*

▷ Witney, in the Cotswolds, has been the home of blanket weaving for about 1,000 years, but today, only one manufacturer survives – Early's of Witney. Proud holders of the Royal Warrant, they have been making blankets since 1669. The traditional designs for their Heritage collection, illustrated, are drawn from their archives, with some of the designs originating from over two hundred years ago. Woven in pure new wool, the blankets and throws are finished in traditional-style blanket stitching. Many other ranges are also available, made from the finest wools, and the company continuously develops new products and colours. For a brochure, contact *Early's of Witney, Witney Mill, Witney, Oxon OX8 5EB. Tel.: 01993-703131.*

◁ Woven by the oldest tweed mill in the Highlands of Scotland, these woollen bed blankets measure 1.8 x 1.5m. Brora also supply a selection of woollen throws and cot blankets, sold by mail order, alongside an extensive range of Scottish cashmere and tweeds. The blankets illustrated cost £75 each, from *Brora, 344 Kings Rd, London SW3 5UR. Tel.: 0171-352 3697.*

△ Pure new wool in rich colours is woven into simple blanket checks to make throws, blankets and bedspreads at an old-established Welsh mill. The throws are made with twisted fringes on two sides, while the full-sized blankets are blanket-stitched all round and the bedspreads are double-woven. All items are available by mail order only, with throws starting at £48, from *Melin Tregwynt, Tregwynt Mill, Castle Morris, Haverfordwest, Pembrokeshire SA62 5UX. Tel.: 01348-891644.*

◁ An Aladdin's Cave of printed fabrics, Celia Birtwell's shop is filled with silks, organzas, voiles, muslins, linens and cottons, for soft furnishings and upholstery. Textiles are hand-printed in classical or contemporary themes: animals, stripes, paisleys and trellises; the animal designs being the best-known. Prices range from £18 to £50 per m. *Celia Birtwell, 71 Westbourne Pk Rd, London W2 5QH. Tel.: 0171-221 0877.*

◁ As their name would suggest, The Monogrammed Linen Shop can embroider initials or emblems on any of their linen, charging from £6 for the service. Made from 100% cotton or linen, their items range from £40 to £300. (The tablecloths illustrated come with matching napkins.) *The Monogrammed Linen Shop, 168 Walton St, London SW3 2JL. Tel.: 0171-589 4033.* Also on the *4th Floor, Harvey Nichols, Knightsbridge, London SW1X 7RJ. Tel.: 0171-235 5000.*

△ A versatile, independent mill, Ousdale Weaving is the most northerly working mill in mainland Scotland, producing woollen scarves, throws, stoles, shawls and hats. Innovative colours and weave effects are based on classic Scottish motifs. The throws come in several colourways in tartan and checks, measure either 1.5 x 2m or 1.5 sq. m and start at £22.50. *Ousdale Weaving Ltd, Ousdale, Berriedale, Caithness KW7 6HD. Tel.: 01431-821371.*

△Carolyn Quartermaine is best known for her use of calligraphy on fabrics, which she hand-prints in gold. To brightly coloured silks, crushed velvets, linens, damasks and cottons, she applies key designs of French and signature script, Mozart manuscript and so on. Fabrics are available from £14 to £91 per m, from her shop, along with her furniture, accessories and collages, and ceramics and glass by Maryse Boxer (see **Ceramics**). *Maryse Boxer and Carolyn Quartermaine, Chez Joseph, 26 Sloane St, London SW1X 7LQ. Tel.: 0171-245 9493.*

▽ This selection of plush and exotic cushions is manufactured by Callan & Horsey, a small company based in Dorset. Employing a variety of antique textiles, including old silk damasks and tapestries, they create an individual range, as well as unusual pincushions. Prices start at £7.50 and rise to £350. For further information, contact *Callan & Horsey, Stone House, Frenchmill La., Shaftesbury, Dorset SP7 0LT. Tel.: 01747-852131.*

◁ Recently launched by Fired Earth (see also **Tiles** and **Flooring**) is a range of timeless fabrics for interiors, including checks and tartans, for curtains and upholstery. The Archive Collection offers crewel work, richly patterned chenilles and tapestry fabric based on 18thC English embroidery. Prices start at £14.99 per m; the Carolean, illustrated, costs £29.99 per m, from *Fired Earth, Twyford Mill, Oxford Rd, Adderbury, Oxon OX17 3HP. Tel.: 01295-812088.*

▷ This sumptuous 'Magnolia Tree with Yellowhammer' was hand-painted on silk by Vivienne Lawes and serves as a door panel. Vivienne draws and paints entirely freehand, employing mostly water-based silk inks on various types of silk, most commonly georgette and crêpe de Chine. Her ties, scarves, waistcoats and cushions cost from £29.50 to £85; her wall-hangings start at £200. *Vivienne Lawes, Unit 7, Gabriel's Wharf, 56 Upper Ground, South Bank, London SE1 9PP. Tel.: 0171-401 2323.*

△ Neil Bottle creates beautiful one-off and limited-edition silks by combining hand-painting, stencilling and printing techniques, applied directly on to the silk. A complex tapestry of images is drawn from life, maps, architecture, figures, shells, botanical drawings and calligraphy. His range, produced to commission only, includes cushions, scarves, ties, waistcoats, wall-hangings and framed prints. The cushions are hand-painted and printed on heavy silk Dupion, measuring 55cm sq., and cost £75 each, including a feather pad + £5 p & p. Contact *Neil Bottle, Tel.: 01843-592953.*

◁ This delicate 'España' silk collage is the work of Helyne Jennings, who employs a range of fabric paints, binders, metallic foils and pigments on the silk, then cuts it and inlays each piece, layering to form the final image. Helyne works to commission and this collage cost £400. *Helyne Jennings, Pennyford Cottage, Burrington, Umberleigh, Devon EX37 9LN. Tel.: 01769-520633.*

△ Influenced by the Victorian era, when pincushions made popular gifts, Katherine Fisher creates her own velvet versions, exquisitely made in a choice of nine colours and five shapes and in two distinct ranges: All Lace is worked freestyle in numerous designs, with decoration in appliquéd laces, pearls and beads; Sampler consists of square and mini shapes, decorated with floral designs or initials worked in fine cross stitch. Also offered is a selection of pendant pincushions to hang on a wall, supplied mounted on decorative card and presented in a gold handmade box. Prices range from £6.95 to about £21. Katherine accepts commissions. For a mail-order catalogue, contact *Katherine Fisher, 369 Holcombe Rd, Greenmount, Bury, Lancs. BL8 4DT. Tel.: 01204-885652.*

▷ Focusing primarily on silk and cotton and employing hand-printing and painting techniques, Camilla Guinness produces cushions, sponge bags, make-up bags and jewellery pouches, as well as one-offs. These cushions cost £45 each, including the pad. A recent addition to her line is printed bedlinen for both adults and children, sporting insect and fruit motifs. Contact *Camilla Guinness, 126 Westbourne Grove, London W11 2RR. Tel.: 0171-221 7949.*

◁ Deeply evocative of Moorish art, the textiles created by Niki Tyson are silk-screened by hand and made to order. Niki applies her designs to viscose, silk, calico, cotton and a host of other fabrics, which are mostly used for soft furnishings. She also produces geometric patterns, consisting of white-on-white and cut-out work. Prices range from about £45 to £70 per m. *Niki Tyson, 4 Waterloo Cottages, Compstall Rd, Romiley, Stockport, Cheshire SK6 4JE. Tel.: 0161-427 7191.*

▷ Reviving a traditional country craft, Pembroke Squares supply handmade bedspreads that are adaptations or copies of Victorian designs collected from all over Britain. Made to order in white or oatmeal cotton, the bedspreads are machine-washable and supplied in six to eight weeks of ordering. Various sizes are offered, with prices starting at £250 for a bedspread of 180 x 240cm. *Pembroke Squares, 28 Westmoreland Pl., London SW1V 4AE. Tel.: 0171-834 9739.*

△ Mail-order suppliers of natural-coloured high-quality cottons, silks, linens, muslins and organzas, The Final Curtain Company will also make up a variety of soft furnishings, either selecting from their own range of fabrics or using those of a customer's choice. Wedding-gift vouchers are also offered. Choose from curtains, blinds, swags and tails, tie-backs, pelmets, tablecloths, bedcovers, valances, piping, frills and loose covers by *The Final Curtain Company, Tel.: 0181-699 3626.*

◁ Liz Lippiatt has been running her own fashion/textile design and print business since 1979 and is a partner in The Textile Workshop in Cirencester, which is her showroom and principal retail outlet. This sofa throw in an exotic-bird design is hand-printed and dyed, costing about £275. The cushions are also hand-printed and dyed, and cost £65 each. *Liz Lippiatt, The Textile Workshop, 7 Brewery Arts, Brewery Ct, Cirencester, Glos. GL7 1JH. Tel.: 01285-656263.*

Mirrors

From the supremely elegant to the definitely different, these mirrors have novel as well as traditional frames, ranging from the shell-encrusted to the carved and gilded.

△ Cas Stanier's stunning circular Golden Flamed Convex Mirror has a red lacquer finish with gilt motifs and supports a pair of candlesticks, a hallmark of her work. Cas trained as a decorative artist, then worked as a gilder and restorer, before starting her own business. She uses traditional skills in her work, drawing on classic styles, but infusing them with her own instinctive and original design ideas. Her pieces are hand-built to her own specifications and decorated using a wide range of techniques. In particular she specializes in diverse gilding effects, complemented with inlays, lacquer and gilt glasswork. The mirror above is 75cm in diameter, and costs £795 (prices for mirrors range from £500 to £1,200). For further details contact *Cas Stanier, Tel.: 0171-229 8017*. See also **Small Furniture**.

▽ Inspired by Moroccan design, the overmantle, wall and full-length mirrors from William Austin's Somerset workshop all have doors or shutters. Some are crackle-glazed over a rich gold patina; others are finished in highly polished black lacquer with fine gold lines; or, like this one, combine both techniques. Prices start from £175 and any size or paint finish can be commissioned. Available through mail order only from *William Austin, 38 Middle Leigh, Street, Somerset BA16 0LH. Tel.: 01458-45281.*

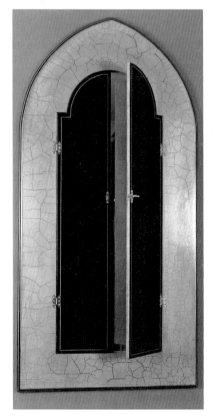

▽ Tom and Diana Langton-Lockton are a husband and wife team, who, employing old methods and materials, design and make mirrors that they hope will become antiques of the future. As this large flamboyant plaster mirror shows, they are inspired by baroque and rococo, but also aim to make their mirrors work in a modern context. This mirror costs £650 with white plaster finish and £850 gilded. To order, *Tel.: 0171-284 1266.*

◁ This beautiful overmantel mirror is handmade by Sasha Bowles Designs, using sheet pewter. Each piece is individually made, working freehand directly on to the pewter. Although known for their mirrors, they also make a range of bathroom cabinets, and are happy to discuss commissions of any kind. Prices start at £50. Contact *Sasha Bowles Designs, Unit 1/2, 46–52 Church Rd, Barnes, London SW13 0DQ. Tel.: 0181-563 1961.*

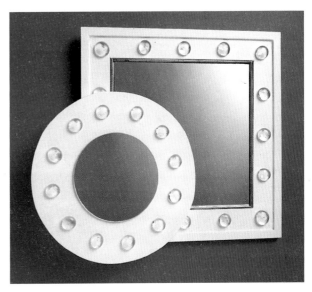

▷ This pretty Cherubs mirror is part of The Lansdowne Collection's range of papier-mâché frames, mirrors and clocks. Handmade and decorated with découpage and crackle-glaze techniques, the mirror is 67 x 53cm and costs £80 + p & p. For catalogue, list of stockists and information about courses, contact *The Lansdowne Collection, 35 Lansdowne Cres., Glasgow G20 6NH. Tel.: 0141-339 6546.* See also **Paint Effects**.

△ Lucy Fielden designs one-off pieces of furniture to commission and works in wood, metal and glass. Part of a collection of lights, mirrors and clocks, these stylish white-painted wood mirrors are simply decorated with smart glass studs. The square mirror measures 33cm and the circular one has a diameter of 25cm. Made to order, they cost £125 each from *Lucy Fielden, Tel.: 0171-259 5108.* Lucy also makes garden furniture (see **The Garden**).

▷ Art History's Large Grotto mirror is sheer rococo. The frame, which can be dragged in a colour of your choice, is encrusted with shells of different sorts, sizes and hues. The colour of the shells can be co-ordinated with your own interior scheme. The mirror is 60cm sq. and costs £185 + p & p. Art History also produce an imaginative range of shelves, planters, pots and firescreens. For a catalogue or to order, contact *Art History Design, The Stable Studios, Nethercott Barton, Iddesleigh, Nr Winkleigh, Devon EX19 8SN. Tel.: 01837-810610.*

▽ Artist and designer Justine Smith not only makes furniture and papier-mâché sculpture, but also specializes in creating beautiful silvered glass panels and mirrors. The panel below measures 45 x 44cm, and incorporates images taken from paintings, pressed flowers and extracts of poetry, which emerge through the silver leaf. Prices start at £80. For further information, contact *Justine Smith, Tel.: 0374-806148 (mobile) or 01823-660855.*

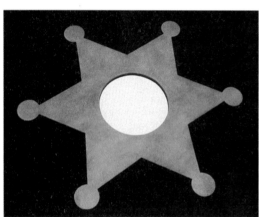

△ A striking crackle-finish mirror from Tors Decorative Artist, who will design and make mirrors of all shapes and sizes, to suit any individual room. They specialize in personalized mirrors bearing coats of arms, crests and sporting motifs with initials. This one costs £90 from *Tors Decorative Artist, Bears, Shepherds Green, Henley-on-Thames, Oxon RG9 4QR. Tel.: 01491-628663.*

◁ Claudia Petley specializes in repoussé, an ancient method of shaping sheet metal where the image emerges out of careful chasing, punching and chiselling. Her fish mirror is a fine example, and reveals her fondness for combining different metals to emphasize colour and texture. Her work ranges from small interior items to large architectural commissions. This mirror costs £350. Contact Claudia at *Lower Nicholson, Docklow, Leominster, Hereford HR6 0SL. Tel.: 01568-760430.*

▷ Fun and richly colourful, this striking papier-mâché wall mirror is by decorative artist Vickie Seal. Among her favourite subjects are fruit, flowers and animals. Other examples are simpler geometric designs. Vickie also accepts commissions. This mirror costs £95. Contact *Vickie Seal, Tel.: 0181-741 4700.*

▽ As her Oak Leaf mirror shows, woodcarver Lynn Hodgson's inspiration comes from the countryside. Her carvings of flora and fauna adorn her mirror frames, boxes, candlesticks, plaques and tables. She enjoys making pieces to commission. This mirror (100 x 50cm) costs £280. Contact Lynn at *Wobage Workshops, Upton Bishop, Ross-on-Wye, Hereford HR9 7QP. Tel.: 01989-780495.*

△ Susan Nelson is a sculptor in stone. She works mainly to commission, uses traditional tools and has the gift of being able to sculpt stone so that it looks as delicate as wood or plaster. Her work includes fire surrounds, lamp bases and mirrors, in a variety of limestones. This mirror, with its circle of finely veined seahorses, their tails entwined, is made from Courtraie, a French limestone. It costs £1,100 (prices start at £850) and can be ordered from *Susan Nelson, Folly Bridge Workshops, Thames St, Oxford OX1 1SU. Tel.: 01865-727203.*

◁ This handsome oval gilded mirror is by Rupert Bevan, who has been gilding, painting and restoring mirrors and furniture for the past ten years, after working as an apprentice for three years. He also designs and makes classical pieces to commission. For prices and further information, contact *Rupert Bevan, 40 Fulham High St, London SW6 3LQ. Tel.: 0171-731 1919.* See also **Upholstered Furniture.**

▷ This glamorous 'Cecilia' mirror is cast in resin from a handmade original, crafted by designers Hampshire & Dillon. Measuring 52cm in diameter, it is available in gold and a variety of striking colours. It costs £89.95, and is part of a collection of contemporary furnishing accessories including cushions, clocks and lamps. For details of stockists or mail order, contact *Hampshire & Dillon, Tel.: 0181-533 1379.*

▽ After graduating from the London College of Furniture, Adam Jackson established his own workshop in Yorkshire, where he makes high-quality bespoke furniture from a vast range of timbers. He aims to supply his customers with precisely what they want. The frame of his elegant Pediment mirror is made from MDF with softwood mouldings and finished with a special crackle-finish paint. It costs £145 + p & p and can be ordered from *Adam Jackson, Poplars Farm, Beningbrough, York YO6 1BY. Tel.: 01904-470842.*

△ Employing the traditional skills of wood-carving and gilding, Alex Jones designs his own pieces like this huge 2.4 x 1.8m mirror. Alex works to commission, approaching each piece with his client very much in mind. He reflects his or her individuality by incorporating representations of their interests into his work – a theatre or a country scene, for example. Alex also specializes in *verre eglomisé,* a technique of gilding and etching glass, which he uses in mirror panels to depict a client's house and garden. Contact *Alex Jones, Elms Lodge, Elms House, Twyford, Hants. SO21 1QF. Tel.: 01962-715115.*

◁ Inspired by Matisse paper cut-outs, this amusing colourful mirror is cast in high-density plaster, and decorated by an inlay technique using coloured plaster, then buffed to a smooth finish. It is also available in terracotta, dark grey and white, and costs about £59. The Works' collection includes cast clocks and mirrors with raised leaf and shell motifs, in natural colours and with rich hand-painted textural effects (see also **Clocks**). For further details, contact *The Works, 110 Chetwynd Rd, London NW5 1DH. Tel.: 0171-267 8215.*

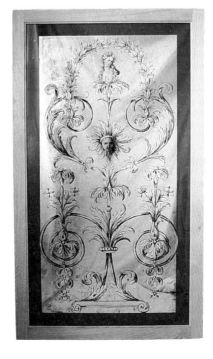

▷ In his Battersea studio, Peter Binnington has revived the ancient art of *verre eglomisé*, the decoration of glass by gilding on the reverse. In this process the gold is engraved with designs and set off by the application of colour. This stunning example shows the depth of colour and intricacy of design that can be combined in one piece. Peter Binnington Workshop undertakes commissions that range from entire rooms panelled in glass to finger plates for doors. The studio has earned a reputation for sensitive restoration and creative new work. Mirrors and prices are available from *Peter Binnington Workshop, 68 Battersea High St, London SW11 3HX. Tel.: 0171-223 9192.*

△ These elegant ornamental mirrors from Belvedere are produced in a subtle antique gilded finish. The three designs shown left to right, Shell, Fruit Basket and Crest, measure 43 x 25cm and cost £39.95 each. They are part of a stylish and comprehensive range of hand-finished furnishing accessories, produced in Belvedere's Hampshire workshops. Gilded and painted frames for mirrors and pictures, as well as an original selection of lamp bases in wood and ceramic, form the main core of production. In addition they import an exciting choice of decorative wall and ceiling lighting from Europe. Order direct from *Belvedere, Unit 3, Hartley Business Park, Selborne, Alton, Hants. GU34 3HS. Tel.: 01420-511524.*

Clocks

Gone are the days of hourglasses. Today, clocks not only tell the time accurately, but are made in a host of different materials: bronze, cardboard, papier mâché, *and even concrete.*

▽ Geometry, colour and pattern are vital elements in Anne Finlay's work, which encompasses jewellery – earrings, brooches, neckpieces and cufflinks – and clocks, her most recent addition. Her stylish, original clocks are folded and curved to create three-dimensional structures in flexible pvc. Of the clocks shown here, the one on the left costs £52, the one on the right, £34; both are available with different coloured details. For a catalogue, contact *Anne Finlay, 7 Bellevue Terr., Edinburgh EH7 4DT. Tel.: 0131-556 3415.*

◁ Assembled in seconds, this is just one in an innovative range of flamboyant three-dimensional clocks from The Cardboard Clock Company. Made from heavy-duty cardboard, each one simply slots together to form a stylish clock with a quartz movement and perfect time keeping. One of three classic styles, the Baroque, illustrated, is 42.5cm high and brings a touch of style to any room. The clocks cost £16 each, including p & p, from *The Cardboard Clock Company, 14 East St, Newton Hill, Wakefield, W. Yorks. WF1 2PY. Tel.: 01924-361544.*

▷ Jenni Robson started out as a jewellery designer, later worked on theatre scenery and displays, and has now turned her talents to clock-making. Her beautiful ceramic and papier-mâché wall clock demonstrates her passion for colour, texture and pattern. Measuring 38.75cm in diameter, it costs £180 (smaller clocks cost from £50) and is available from *Tic Tok Design, 162 Barrow Rd, Sileby, Loughborough, Leics. LE12 7LR. Tel.: 01509-814803.* Jenni also makes frames and mirrors and works to commission.

△ Partners Don McCollin and Maureen Bryan produce unusual, elegant accessories in cast concrete. Each piece is cast from a hand-carved original and has a unique stone-like quality. In some of their designs, the concrete is gilded; see, for example, the clock and lamp above. Prices start at £40. Visit their showroom or contact *McCollin Bryan, 113a Commercial St, London E1 6BG. Tel.: 0171-247 7044.*

▽ The perfect gift for a golfer which could become a collector's item as well, Roger Lascelles' Novel Golfer's Clock has its quartz movement cleverly concealed inside a traditional xlb tea tin. The charming label on the hinged lid features a golfer at St. Andrews c.1700 and the dial shows a game in progress over the Old Course with the town in the background. One in an impressive range of original alarm, mantel, desk, tin, wall and table clocks, it is available in green, as shown, or blue, and inside is the added bonus of a quality golf ball and six tees. For further information, catalogue and price list, contact *Roger Lascelles Clocks Ltd, 29 Carnwath Rd, London SW6 3HR. Tel.: 0171-731 0072.*

◁ Fio's wall clock in poppy red has a satin finish and a subtle domed profile. It is available in graphic as well as the numbered dials shown, measures 25cm in diameter, and is available in other colours and finishes. Priced at £31.99 (including p & p), it can be ordered by sending a cheque for the full amount to *Fio Design Associates, 1302 Custard Factory, Gibb St, Digbeth, Birmingham B9 4AA. Tel./Fax: 0121-608 6066.*

▽ Donald Yule's wide variety of ceramic clock designs includes kitchen, ships', Hickory Dickory and crackle-glazed clocks, all equally at home in modern and traditional settings. Faces can be personalized for weddings and businesses, and prices range from £16.95 to £60. They are supplied by mail order in shock-proof boxes with a one year guarantee and free battery. For a free colour brochure, contact *Donald Yule, 23A Trowbridge Rd, Bradford on Avon, Wilts. BA15 1EE. Tel.: 01225-862693.*

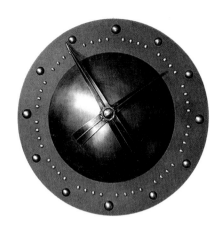

◁ Marianne Forrest combines different materials and metals in her clocks to striking effect. Here, the patinated bronze domed centre creates a feeling of depth, accentuated by the contrasting composite surround; the studs are made of polished brass and steel. The clock costs £2,000. Marianne also makes pocket and wrist watches. For further information, contact her at *Studio 16, Clocktower Workspace, 4 Shearling Way, London N7 9TH. Tel.: 0171-609 6621.* (No callers without an appointment.)

▷ Trained as a 3D designer, Louise Byrne works in wood and metal, making clocks and cabinets, suitable for wall or mantlepiece. As this clock reveals, Louise is inspired by the beach; both by objects weathered by the sea and found on the shore and by the contrasting brightly coloured seaside deckchairs, beach huts, Punch and Judy theatres and fairgrounds. Her clock costs £125 + p & p by mail order from *28 Firwood Ave., Urmston, Manchester M41 9PJ. Tel.: 0161-865 9843.*

△ If you would like a Gloucester Old Spot Pig on your desk or a Light Sussex Hen on your dresser, which also keep perfect time, then consider HandMade in Wiltshire. They produce a unique collection of hand-crafted clocks in the shape of farm and rare breed animals, which can stand on a table or hang on a wall. For further details and prices, contact *HandMade in Wiltshire, Sandiacres, Etchilhampton, Devizes, Wilts. SN10 3JP. Tel.: 01380-860214.*

◁ A fresh, natural design, inspired by seashore finds, this pretty shell clock from The Works is cast from high-density industrial plaster with a white finish. It also comes in terracotta and verdigris, measures 24cm in diameter and costs about £42. Shell mirrors are also available. The Works' collection includes clocks and mirrors, cast with earth pigments or decorated with rich hand-painted textural effects (see also **Mirrors**). For further details, contact *The Works, 110 Chetwynd Rd, London NW5 1DH. Tel.: 0171-267 8215.*

▽ A collection of handmade, distressed Kentucky clocks from Appalachia, the shop that specializes in American folk art. Made to a traditional American design, these attractive clocks have reliable battery-operated quartz movements, and are available both from the shop and by mail order. The large clock is 22.5cm in height and costs £34.99 + p & p; the small one is 17.5cm and costs £24.99 + p & p. Both come in green, light blue, wine and navy. Pure cotton blanket throws, Shaker-inspired prints, homespun garlands and other hanging decorations – peg-rail dolls, handcarved mermaids and wooden hearts – and hand-painted Shaker stacking boxes are just some of the other items for sale. For a free mail-order brochure, telephone *Appalachia, 14a George St, St. Albans, Herts. AL3 4ER. Tel.: 01727-836796.*

CLOCKS

▷ Toucans perch on top of and a fish hangs below this zany ceramic wall clock by talented designer Kate Brett. Measuring 26cm high and 18cm wide, it costs £89 + p & p, and is available from *Mildred Pearce, 33 Earlham St, Covent Garden, London WC2H 9LD. Tel.: 0171-379 5128.* Visit the store, which is crammed with original decorative accessories, or telephone for an equally inspiring mail-order catalogue. See also **Ceramics** and **Decorative Accessories**.

▽ The clocks in this smart range from ZeD are designed by David Yarnell. Handmade from MDF and hand-painted, each clock shape is available in the six colours illustrated. They cost £35 each, including p & p, and come individually boxed and fitted with a high-quality, guaranteed German quartz movement. There are 75 different clocks in ZeD's current range, available by mail order from *ZeD Clock Company, 23 New Mount St, Manchester M4 4DE. Tel: 0161-953 4054.*

Decorative Accessories

So much of the character and individuality of a home comes from the miscellaneous objects that fill it – the bits and pieces that we all collect, from candlesticks and collages to boxes and bookends.

△ Scented candles in hand-thrown pots, made by Coldpiece Pottery, with fragrances created by quality essences in a choice of tuberose, honeysuckle, citronella, cinnamon and clove, and oriental spice. Prices start at £6 for the smallest flowerpot (7 x 7cm), rising to £45 for a large bowl (27 x 11.5cm). Various garden accessories are also available, such as a wide selection of flowerpots, orchid pots, seed trays, and so on. For mail-order information, contact *Coldpiece Pottery, Hound Green, Hook, Hants. RG27 8LQ. Tel.: 01734-326540.*

▷ Evocative of early 19thC decoration and the Brighton Pavilion, this wall light from the Monica Pitman Collection (see also **Tables and Chairs** and **Lighting**) is made entirely from metal. It can either be used with candles (as shown) or it can be wired; it matches a six-light chandelier, complete with monkeys. Hand-painted with the utmost care, to incorporate a convincing bamboo effect, this wall light achieves an authentic look. Measuring 50cm high and 32cm wide, it costs £348 and is only one example of the fine metal lighting, furniture and accessories available from this supplier. For a brochure, contact *The Monica Pitman Collection, M5 Chelsea Garden Market, Chelsea Harbour, London SW10 0XE. Tel.: 0171-376 3180.*

△ Designed to hang on a wall or sit on a sideboard, this candle cabinet in oak (from managed forests) contains an elongating candle holder. It comes in dark (as shown) or natural finishes, complete with eight ivory candles and an antique-brass snuffer. Measuring 43 x 37 x 26cm, it costs £189. A one-door version costs £149. Other wooden accessories include sconces, candle boxes, letter racks, and cutlery trays and boxes. For a mail-order catalogue, contact *Yellow House, Pyes Mill, Station Rd, Bentham, Lancaster LA2 7LJ. Tel.: 015242-62938.*

▽ This chandelier, together with its accompanying wall lights, forms the Classical Wrought-Iron range by Porta Romana, available in antiqued gold leaf (as shown), antiqued silver leaf, rust and leaded black with gold leaf. The chandelier is 55cm high x 55cm wide, and comes with three to six arms. It costs £320. The other wall lights and small 'Regency' mirror light (bottom left) range in price from £110 to £240. Porta Romana also supply a painted range from Italy (chandeliers, wall lights and lamp bases) in a 'fresco' finish in four colourways. They also produce their own lamp bases, mirrors and furniture, hand-crafted in the UK. (Themes are Classical and Provençal.) For a catalogue and information on stockists, contact *Porta Romana, Lower Froyle, Alton, Hants. GU34 4LS. Tel.: 01420-23005.*

▷ Colour is an essential ingredient in the vibrant one-off paper collages created by Amanda Pearce (see also **Screens**), which she hand-paints. After ripping and cutting the papers, she works into them using an ink-imprinting process and oil pastels to produce further layers and textures. Her work is sold all over the world and prices start at £50. She welcomes commissions. *Amanda Pearce, 74 Carlingford Rd, Hucknall, Notts. NG15 7AG. Tel.: 0115-963 8440.*

▽ A tribute to gastronomy, this 3-D collage is produced by Mandy Pritty, who favours themes such as the garden, the seashore and the arts. She welcomes commissions for personalized pieces, too, based upon any person, place, subject or era. Each collage is unique and set in its own specially designed glazed box-frame. Simple compositions start at £75; 'story' collages at £130; from *Mandy Pritty, 76 Carysfort Rd, London N16 9AP. Tel.: 0171-249 0038 or 01956-368462.*

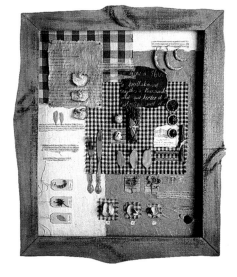

△ Ten years ago, Acres Farm revived the idea of fitting small shades on brass holders to candles. Today they stock dozens of different designs for both holders and candle-shades. The shades are fashioned from card, parchment, parchment card, laminated fabrics (cottons and silks), glass and metal, and translucent PVC, all decorated by hand in countless ways. Available from retailers in most major towns and cities in the UK. Contact *Acres Farm, Bradfield, Reading, Berks. RG7 6JH. Tel.: 01734-744305.*

◁ Representing the cream of British and Irish ceramic design, the Mildred Pearce Collection includes over 150 different pieces in truly original designs, offering alternative gift ideas (see also **Ceramics** and **Clocks**). A recently launched mail-order service makes readily available a wealth of items, from unusual scent bottles and clocks to gargantuan cups with hand-painted faces, and bizarre candlesticks such as these by Robyn Wilkinson. Costing £49.50 each, the striped one stands 40cm high, the spotted, 36cm. Visit the emporium or apply for a mail-order catalogue from *Mildred Pearce, 33 Earlham St, London WC2H 9LD. Tel.: 0171-379 5128.*

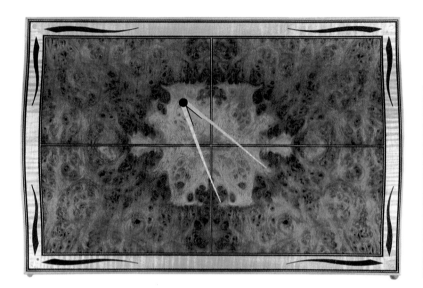

Andrew Crawford works to commission, handmaking exquisite boxes from the finest materials, in traditional and contemporary styles. He can produce a box for almost any storage purpose, from playing cards to musical instruments, and to budgets large and small, from about £50 to £3,500 or more. The curved pencil box (top left and bottom) is made from burr oak, with detailing in boxwood, dyed veneers, fiddle-back maple and mother-of-pearl, and the whole is French polished. Inside are six trays to accommodate assorted pencils and crayons, and much other drawing equipment. Measuring 32.5 x 22.5 x 15cm, it cost £2,450. The multi-coloured harlequin tea caddy (top right) is decorated in dyed veneers, with detailing in kingwood, boxwood and ebony. The interior comprises two tea boxes in burr oak and a handmade lead crystal blending bowl. Finished with French polish, the box measures 35 x 25 x 17.5cm and cost £2,650. *Andrew Crawford, Unit BO2, Acton Business Centre, School Rd, London NW10 6TD. Tel.: 0181-961 7066.*

▷ Highly sought-after, fine boxes by Colin Jones reflect time-honoured wood-working skills. He offers a huge range of boxes, from £21 to £1,200, and accepts commissions. Some of his pieces, such as this one, feature hand-cut marquetry. All are lined with a choice of pure cotton velvets or suedes, in various colours. He supplies almost any combination of insert, tray and lock; also a specialist restoration service for antique boxes. For a brochure, contact *Young Jones, 'Wooden World', Bryn St, Newtown, Powys SY16 2HW. Tel.: 01686-624081.*

▽ Vegetable-tanned leathers are cut, stitched and hand-finished by Wytske Lazenby to produce high-quality cases and boxes, to commission and to special requirements. Jewellery cases, spirit flasks, briefcases, games boxes, writing cases and trunks are all within her range, each lined with a choice of suedes, silks or finely woven cloths. Prices start at £70 and increase to £1,000 for a sturdy trunk. *The Glanarrow Box Company, Glanarrow Mill, Eardisland, Hereford HR6 9BY. Tel.: 01544-388403.*

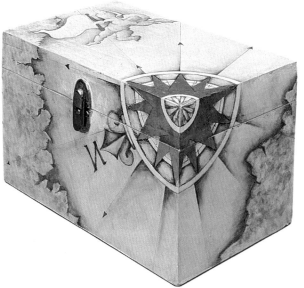

△ Hollie Beavis focuses on themes such as antique maps, geometry and paintings by Gustav Klimt to decorate her boxes. She uses gesso, watercolour and gilding, and prices range from £30 to £300. Hollie's work is also displayed in Fisherton Mill in Salisbury and she welcomes commissions. Contact her by telephone on *0181-642 0790.*

◁ This large box is hand-painted by *trompe-l'œil* specialist, Amanda Baird. She has lined the interior with trays and decorative paper. The box measures 27.5 x 20cm and 15cm high; it costs £270. Amanda also makes hand-painted mirror cases, pencil holders and small wall cabinets. For a brochure, contact *Amanda Baird, Barford Cliff Cottage, Downton, Salisbury, Wilts. SP5 3QF. Tel.: 01725-511146.*

▷ A well-established basketware company produces a broad selection of items, handmade from highest-quality Somerset willow. As well as log baskets (more available, £18.95-£43), they make furniture, accessories for the kitchen, picnic hampers, animal carriers, and a host of other useful and decorative items for the home and garden (see also **Kitchen Accessories**). For a mail-order catalogue, contact *P.H. Coate & Son, Meare Green Court, Stoke St. Gregory, Taunton, Somerset TA3 6HY. Tel.: 01823-490249.*

▽ This vibrant 'Athenian Ariel' screen is one of a range from 0 IV Screens. For use as a room or fire screen, it is hand-painted and part of a range that starts at £105 and includes a variety of sizes. For a mail-order catalogue, contact *O IV Screens, 2 Bangalore St, London SW15 1QE. Tel.: 0181-785 6407.*

△ Screen-printed with acrylic paint and hand-finished with silk matt varnish, this fire screen is strong and will not fade or warp in sunlight. Made from 9mm MDF, it measures 61cm high x 60cm wide and fits an average-sized fireplace. The Gloucester old-spot (illustrated; £45) is extremely popular, as are screens depicting racing colours chosen by a client (£60). Larger or smaller screens can be custom-made and painted in a variety of designs. Contact *Amanda Leschallas, M.C. Arts, Moatwood Cottage, Gifford's Lane, Wickhambrook, Newmarket, Suffolk CB8 8PQ. Tel.: 01440-820211.*

◁ A selection of accessories by Sue Bensassi. Her footstools are made to order (this one is 45 x 45 x 30cm and costs £120). She produces and custom-makes hatboxes with padded lids, silk cord handles and co-ordinating lining. Prices start at £35. Her wooden invitation boards (£18) are padded and fabric-covered; and her keyring boards (£12) feature fleur-de-lis hooks. Contact *Sue Bensassi, 4c Calderon Place, London W10 6QJ. Tel.: 0181-964 4920.*

▽ Integrity and care are evident in this pair of bookends, extraordinary reproductions of the Baden Baden Theatre, originally built in 1860. Made from British gypsum plaster, each piece is unique, being hand-cast and hand-finished, with added window-frame detail in etched brass. These bookends weigh 3.1kg, are 19cm high and cost £70 a pair. Timothy Richards also makes mirrors and a range of larger signed architectural models, retailing at between £120 and £200. Timothy is gaining an international reputation for his highly collectable work, having been commissioned by Sir Terence Conran, two Royal Palaces and the Spanish Government, among others. Contact *Timothy Richards Architectural Fine Art Commissions, 59 West View Rd, Keynsham, Bristol BS18 1BQ. Tel.: 0117-986 2318.*

◁ The dumb waiter comes in many disguises from Allia Design, whose characters are individually handmade in MDF (1.2m tall) and painted by hand, with a heavy metal base. An ever-increasing choice includes a butler, maidservant, knight, jockey and chef, to name but a few. Each is equipped with a tray to carry any number of items, or a display holder, for menus, and so on. Each can be painted in the colours of your choice, and a new character produced to commission. Prices start at £185 + p & p. For a brochure, contact *Allia Design, The Black Cabin Barn, Hailes, Cheltenham, Glos. GL54 5PB. Tel.: 01242-603165.*

▽ Shells, driftwood, coral, sponges, starfish and seahorses adorn this original hand-crafted 40cm swag. Trained and best known as floral designers, Jennifer Armstrong and Keith Powers also create fresh and dried-flower arrangements, kitchen swags, wall hangings, shell-encrusted baskets, garlands and candle pots. This swag costs £30, from *Armstrong & Powers, 20 Upper Tooting Park, London SW17 7SR. Tel.: 0181-767 0758.*

◁ These appealing wooden planters constructed from English oak (from sustainable sources) double up as fruit bowls, pot-pourri containers and so on, and measure 10 x 22 x 22cm, costing £44.50 each. They are designed and made by Erica Wolfe-Murray for her mail-order company, Touch Design (see also **Tableware**), which supplies made-to-last accessories for the home and garden, in fresh classic shapes, crafted from cotton, wood, terracotta, wicker, wire and glass. For a catalogue, contact *Touch Design, PO Box 60, Andover, Hants. SP11 6SS. Tel.: 01264-738060.*

▷ Skilfully and richly painted by hand, this is the work of Katie Potter. Using paint, gold leaf and special glazes, and drawing on themes such as flowers, fruit and animals, Katie transforms furniture and household and garden objects, from bread bins and buckets to coal scuttles and cupboards. She sells a standard range (£42-120) and a variety of one-offs. She welcomes commissions and runs courses in furniture painting. *Katie Potter, The Granary Studio, Palmersmoor House, Iver, Bucks. SL0 9LG. Tel.: 01753-651077.*

△ Anna Nockolds (see also **Kitchen Accessories**) creates innovative hand-painted letter racks in seven different designs, costing £35 + £4 p & p. As well as this teacup and willow-pattern plate, she makes racks featuring flowerpots, pigs, a fish and fishing bag, and a rabbit. Incorporated into most of the racks is the name and address of the person buying it, or of the person to whom it is to be given. Anna can also decorate racks with portraits of people's homes, taken from photographs, for £45, and will undertake other special commissions. For a brochure, contact *Anna Nockolds, The Old Laundry, Church Hill, Starston, Harleston, Norfolk, IP20 9PF. Tel.: 01379-852424.*

▷ Based in West Sussex, Ribbons & Bows specialize in traditional flat-work découpage on hat-boxes, fire screens, room dividers in four sections, bed-heads and waste bins. Prices start at £27 for a small hat-box, rising to £275 for a room divider. Courses in découpage are also offered, with not more than six people in a class, from £49 for one day; also kits for £15 + p & p. Contact *Ribbons & Bows, 19 East St, Petworth, W. Sussex GU28 0AB. Tel.: 01798-344088.*

▽ Skilfully employing the techniques of découpage, crackelure and gilding, Tennille Dix creates items such as coasters, bottle-holders, trays, shades, jardinières and waste-paper baskets, all made of metal. Her outlets include Thomas Goode and Harvey Nichols, and themes consist of animals, flowers, and Italian and Chinese motifs, but she can work to a client's design and colours. Price range £25-150. For a brochure, contact *Tennille Designs, 21 Gilston Rd, London SW10 9SJ. Tel.: 0171-351 0059.*

△ A leading designer and producer of high-quality hand-painted toleware (metal) cachepots, jardinières and waste bins, Monique Shaw offers both classic and contemporary designs. The latter include leopard and zebra patterns, stripes, tartan, and stars and suns. The classical choice (small sample shown) includes tortoiseshell, brocade, vine leaves, acanthus, a variety of floral themes and traditional dolphin designs. Rich colours are often combined with gold to striking effect. For a list of stockists, contact *Monique Shaw Designs, 57 Claudia Pl., London SW19 6ES. Tel.: 0181-789 7622.*

◁ From table mats to four-poster beds, Jane Gordon-Smith creates beautiful découpage items to order. As well as supplying many interior-design shops in the UK, she exports to Europe and the USA, and teaches at art centres. A 25cm mat costs £12; trays from £25; glove-boxes from £98; head-boards from £250; and screens from £450. For more details on commissions or a list of stockists, contact *Jane Gordon-Smith, Yew Glen House, Castle St, Mere, Wilts. BA12 6JE. Tel.: 01747-860865.*

▽ Traditional colours combined with 18th and 19thC prints of botanical and other natural-history themes inspire Maggie Philo's work. Her eye-catching collection of découpaged metalware includes planters, trays, buckets, watering cans and other items for the home. Each piece is unique and looks old. Maggie also sells découpaged Shaker boxes and parchment flowers made by hand, and is developing new designs. Her work costs £18-80; she also runs courses on découpage and furniture-painting. *Maggie Philo, 18 Walpole Rd, Kemp Town, Brighton BN2 2EA. Tel.: 01273-696405.*

▽ A firm believer in any person's ability to succeed in crafts, Veronica Mills runs one-day courses. Each person works in an informal, friendly atmosphere, in a small group, and can expect to take at least one finished piece of work home. Crafts offered are: papier mâché, rag-rugs, wreaths and garlands, and decorative effects. The courses cost £38 per person. *Veronica Mills, Paradise House, 1 Queen Sq., Cullompton, Devon EX15 1DB. Tel.: 01884-32462.*

◁ Embellished with an inlaid découpage surround, this delightful papier mâché panel by decorative artist Val Roet is hand-painted in oils and gouache and measures 20 x 25cm. Val's collection also consists of jewellery, mirrors and candlesticks, with prices ranging from £25 to £125. She also offers a one-day workshop each week. *Val Roet, 29 Upper Pk Rd, Kingston, Surrey KT2 5LB. Tel.: 0181-546 5243.*

Kitchen Accessories and Tableware

Larders, egg cupboards, knife blocks, pepper mills and trays... this section is brimming with novel ideas for the heart of your house.

△ Hayloft Woodwork crafted this island work-table from elm and MDF, incorporating in the design a slatted base shelf and tongue-and-groove sides. Custom-built, as is all their furniture, it starts at £1,200. As well as traditional kitchens, bedrooms and bathrooms, they design and make alcove bookcases, wardrobes, beds, nurseries, studies, radiator covers, offices and boardrooms (see **Storage**). *Hayloft Woodwork, 3 Bond St (off Chiswick High Rd), London W4 1QZ. Tel.: 0181-747 3510.*

▽ Incorporated within this 3-m distress-painted island unit are a maple endgrain chopping block, a pull-out bin and pan drawers. Made to commission, it costs £4,000-5,000, depending on specifications. Stephen Coe employs the very best kiln-dried timber and traditional mortice and tenon joints in doors and frames, plus dove-tailed drawers as standard. He makes all types of fitted and free-standing furniture, including bespoke kitchens, tables, dressers and bedroom cabinets. For further information, contact *Stephen Coe, 10 Beaufoy Close, The Sycamores, Shaftesbury, Dorset SP7 8PT. Tel.: 01747-855190.*

◁ Combining the traditional and the innovative, Howard Robinson and George Cornish provide a specialist design and cabinet-making service. Known for their kitchens, they also undertake work in other rooms, including conservatories. This free-standing solid beech food cupboard cost £2,500. *Robinson and Cornish, Southay House, Oakwood Close, Roundswell, Barnstaple, Devon EX31 3NJ. Tel.: 01271-329300.*

▽ Hermitage Furniture supply untreated pine accessories with a paint treatment for you to create your own finish. A butler's tray, wall cupboard, shelf unit, bath rack and trug can all be dyed in one of 23 hues, limed, gilded or polished. Treatments start at £2.98 for 250ml of dye. The tray and trug cost £20 each and the wall cupboard £55 (ready-finished for £5 extra) by mail order from *Hermitage Furniture, The Hermitage, 6 Castle Rd, Sandgate, Kent CT20 3AG. Tel.: 01303-248114.*

△ Simple worktop storage is provided by this rustic wooden egg cupboard, the Henstridge Egg Tower, which is made and painted by hand in a choice of seven colours. It holds 12 eggs, measures 38cm high x 18cm long x 15.5cm wide and costs £35. Orchard specialize in handmade contemporary furniture, pottery, linen, glassware, candlesticks and frames (see **Small Furniture**). They have two shops (one in Salisbury) and a mail-order service. *Orchard, 14 Mill Lane, Wimborne, Dorset BH21 1LN. Tel.: 01202-848849.*

▷ Robust and made to last, these practical food larders and the inimitable mini-egg cupboard are part of a range of unusual distress-painted wooden decorative accessories and small furniture, for use in the home and garden (see also **The Garden**). Crafted from softwoods from managed forests, they are built as free-standing items, but can also be wall-mounted and most are fitted with carrying handles. Prices range from £34.95 to £113.55 + p & p. Herb boxes, trays, wine carriers and library steps are just some of the other items available by mail order only from *Somerset Creative Products, Charlecote, Mark, Somerset TA9 4PX. Tel.: 01278-641622.*

These attractive knife blocks in solid wood and painted in colourful checks (shown below) are handmade by Swanalong and cost £29.99. Colours that are unlisted in their standard range are available, at an extra charge of £7. This company produces numerous hand-painted wooden products for the home, many of them decorated with cut-out people, animals and flowers, ranging from £10 to £100. They make letter racks, trays, waste bins, egg racks, boxes for kitchen utensils, personalized pencil pots and so on. Typical themes include teddy bears, cats, labradors and children. Their unusual kitchen-paper holders (see right) are decorated with animals or flowers and stand 35cm high. A photograph of a client's pet or child can be scanned to scale to decorate an item. For a brochure and mail-order details, contact *Swanalong, Middle Farm, Taston, Charlbury, Oxford OX7 3JL. Tel.: 01608-811072.*

▽ Dedicated to producing the finest pepper and salt mills possible, Robert Smith and his small company carefully select timber to ensure a product that will last for generations. Each mill is individually turned and finished by hand, then fitted with a mechanism made by Peugeot. Prices range from £10 each to £150 per pair. For further information, contact *Robert Smith, 1 Homeleigh, Whempstead, Ware, Herts. SG12 0PL. Tel.: 01920-830478.*

◁ These kitchen or bar stools are crafted from ash and contain a special hole in the centre of the seat, to facilitate lifting. Made by Tim Wood (see also **Cupboards and Chests** and **Beds**), they cost £139 each. Tim has spent many years developing another extremely pleasing design, which features a back to the stool. For more details, contact *Tim Wood Furniture Ltd, 41 Ballantine St, London SW18 1AL. Tel.: 0181-875 1638.*

▷ Founded in 1819, P.H. Coate & Son (see also **Decorative Accessories**) produce basketware from the highest-quality Somerset willow. Their picnic baskets come in a variety of designs, with only a selection illustrated here. Prices start at £20, rising to £70. A huge range of other basketware items are made. For a brochure, send an s.a.e. to *P.H. Coate & Son, Meare Green Ct, Stoke St. Gregory, Taunton, Somerset TA3 6HY. Tel.: 01823-490249.*

△ These wooden egg racks are hand-crafted by Anna Nockolds (see also **Decorative Accessories**) and painted by hand, with other colours available. They cost £35 for the smaller version (to hold six eggs) and £40 for the larger (to contain a dozen) + £4.50 p & p. Anna's Country Collection includes dummy boards, fire screens and numerous decorative accessories for the home. For a colour brochure, contact *Anna Nockolds, The Old Laundry, Unit 3, Church Hill, Starston, Harleston, Norfolk IP20 9PF. Tel.: 01379-852424.*

▽ A novel and award-winning concept in place-mat design. Sarah Cavendish makes and paints by hand jigsaw-puzzle centrepieces, which can be used as a whole to protect a dining-table when not in use or as a set of table mats during mealtimes. Sarah has created a number of different interlocked shapes, designed specifically for use as place mats and coasters. Fashioned from 6mm-thick MDF, the mats are decorated, then finished with a heatproof lacquer and a brightly coloured felt base. Sarah can make centrepieces to commission in many shapes, sizes and decorative designs. A set costs about £60, from *Sarah Cavendish, 150 Park Rd, London W4 3HP. Tel.: 0181-994 2950.*

△ Lois Carr has specialized in creating lively hand-painted table mats since 1987. Each one is painted freehand, with themes such as sunflowers, fruit and vegetables, and pansies. Resistant to hot plates and boiling water, the mats are backed with felt and need only a wipe with a damp cloth and an occasional rub with furniture polish. Prices start at £8.50 each and rectangular mats are also available. Lois welcomes commissions. Contact *Lois Carr, Quedley Copse, Flimwell, Wadhurst, E. Sussex TN5 7NY. Tel.: 01580-879357.*

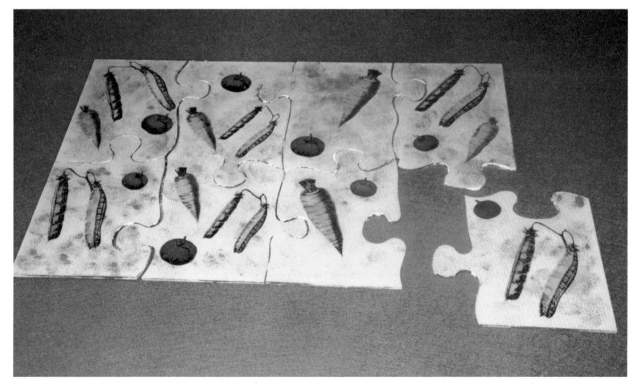

▽ These handmade, minimalist glass trays feature a sand-blasted patterned base, edged in maple, and finished with brass handles. The 4mm-thick toughened glass can carry most items, apart from exceptionally hot and heavy ones. A small tray (32 x 32cm) costs £65; a large one (40 x 54cm) £85. Touch Design (see also **Decorative Accessories**) design and make simple, classic home-furnishing and garden accessories, all from natural materials. For a mail-order catalogue, contact *Touch Design Ltd, PO Box 60, Andover, Hants. SP11 6SS. Tel.: 01264-738060.*

▽ These bejewelled napkin rings are fashioned from resin decorated with gold, then encrusted with fake pearls and diamanté, to glamorous effect. Co-ordinating photograph frames, candlesticks, candelabra and jewellery are also offered and commissions undertaken to include mirrors and small boxes. *Loretta Scott, Tel.: 0171-436 0734.*

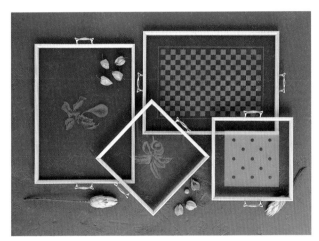

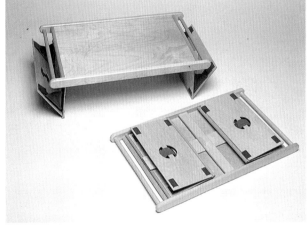

△ Amanda Harman's breakfast tray folds completely flat but, when open, its wood-and-canvas side pockets expand to hold magazines, newspapers, writing materials and so on. The tray comes with natural canvas side pockets or, as illustrated, with red pocket straps and green sides. It costs £120 and is just one of several space-saving designs, including furniture, by *Amanda Harman, 46 Epirus Rd, London SW6 7UH. Tel.: 0171-381 2282.*

▷ A small selection of the variety of hand-painted tableware items made by Occasional Art, whose trays, place mats and coasters are crafted from MDF, decorated, then lacquered to render them heat- and stain-resistant. Themes include a full range of farm animals, various fruits and sunflowers. They will also paint specific designs to order. Prices start at £20 for trays; £10 for a set of six coasters; and £25 for a set of six place mats, from *Occasional Art, 176 Ffordd-y-Parc, Litchard, Bridgend, Mid Glam. CF31 1RA. Tel.: 01656-669662.*

Crafts for Children

A child's room needs to be bright and sunny with colourful fabrics, fun furniture and interesting toys, all of which are illustrated here.

Two brothers, Tony and Marc Stevenson, began to produce rocking horses in 1982, and so far have made over 1,500 and restored almost as many, with customers all over the world. Driven by a desire to produce the best rocking horses possible, they build theirs to last, paying great attention to detail and using only timber sourced from plantations with a sound replanting policy. The traditional-looking horses are carved from the best kiln-dried timber, decorated with hand-stitched leather tack and real horsehair for tail and mane. A broad range of finishes includes a dappled effect or natural wood (walnut, illustrated below, oak, shown right, or mahogany). The Stevenson Brothers also make horses to commission and supply an ever-increasing range of other hand-crafted toys, from enchanting dolls' houses to rocking animals. Visitors to the workshop are welcome. For a brochure, contact *Stevenson Brothers, The Workshop, Ashford Rd, Bethersden, Ashford, Kent TN26 3AP. Tel.: 01233-820363/820772.*

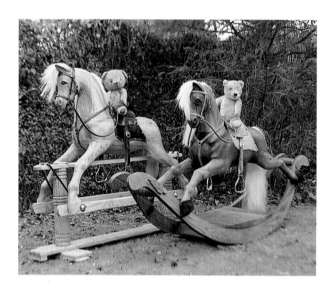

△ Alan Lees works to commission to create a wide variety of Victorian-style horses, both free-standing and rocking. Hand-carved from quality hardwoods (usually from sustainable sources), they are fixed to bows (rockers) or safety stands. Manes and tails are made from real horsehair, and a client chooses the colours; tack is handmade in leather. Alan also offers a sensitive restoration service and undertakes other large sculptural wood-carving commissions. Horses range in price from £1,000 to £2,500. Contact *Alan and Catherine Lees, 38 Patna Rd, Kirkmichael, Ayrshire KA19 7PJ. Tel.: 01655-750386.*

△ Based on the style and elegance of their Georgian and Victorian ancestors, the wooden rocking horses supplied by Haddon Ltd are constructed by hand to make strong and durable toys. The horses come complete with real horsehair mane and tail, and with fully removable leather tack. Different sizes, styles and colours are offered with either a bow rocker or pillar stand. Prices start at £520. For a catalogue of these and other hand-crafted wooden toys and gifts, made in the UK, contact *Haddon Ltd, 5 Telford Rd, Clacton-on-Sea, Essex CO15 4LP. Tel.: 01255-424745.*

△ An ingenious idea, this custom-made petrol pump opens up to reveal a cupboard containing adjustable shelves. This version stands 2.3m high x 35cm wide and is crafted to a high standard from Canadian yellow pine and mahogany, with a hose fashioned from rope. Jim Crockatt (see also **Tables and Chairs** and **Cupboards and Chests**) has finished the whole piece in teak oil and waxed it to a fine water-resistant shine. *Jim Crockatt, Pococks Cottage, Mariners Lane, Bradfield, Berks. RG7 6HX. Tel.: 01734-744728.*

△ Makers of traditional wooden toys, boxes and accessories, Jigsaw decorate their boxes with hand-painted figures fixed in relief on to background scenes. Select from teddy bears, soldiers, trains, ducks or clowns. Boxes can be custom-made with a child's name painted on to the lid, or an engraved brass plate fitted inside. Measuring 80 x 45 x 40cm, the boxes start at £140. Traditional panelled boxes are made to order in any timber or size required, with a name or wording carved into the panel or lid. For a brochure and more information, contact *Jigsaw, Llanfairynghornwy, Gwynedd LL65 4LW. Tel.: 01407-730620.*

△ This hand-painted toy box is part of a wide range of brightly coloured quality children's furniture, crafted from pine and MDF and supplied by mail order by The Children's Room. Toy boxes start at £145, with themes including the circus, sealife, the farm, the garden and a clown alphabet, or a folk-art motif can be applied by hand. Furniture in MDF includes display units, bedside tables, wardrobes, bookshelves and toy cupboards. Contact *The Children's Room, North St, Langport, Somerset TA10 9RH. Tel.: 01458-252338.*

◁ Janey Hillsborough and Hannah Doherty source exclusive, handmade, wooden and other traditional toys designed to stand the test of time and suit a variety of budgets. The Hill Toy Company operates through a Christmas shop in Kensington, a mail-order service and agents across the UK, and undertakes commissions. Their dolls' house collection consists of a one-room house for £49.95; a small house for £85; and a town house for £145. Furniture and a family of four are also available. For a catalogue, contact *The Hill Toy Co., PO Box 2963, London W11 2LF. Tel.: 0171-229 0222.*

▷ A small family business, The Camno Workshop designs traditional toys, handmaking them from top-quality materials with fine detail. As well as dolls' houses, the company makes carved hobby horses, rocking horses, cribs, stilts, name puzzles, forts, farms and garages. The houses are fashioned from plywood to ensure both strength and lightness, in the following designs: Traditional, Town House, Victorian and Georgian. They are supplied either decorated or undecorated and a range of exquisite miniature reproduction furniture is also offered. Special features can be applied to any toy or house, and commissions are gladly accepted. (Miniature replicas of clients' homes are especially popular.) Dolls' houses from stock start at £68.50. For a catalogue, contact the *Camno Workshop, Railway Cottage, Camno Crossing, by Newtyle, Angus PH12 8SW. Tel.: 01828-640375.*

▷ Based in Wiltshire, Adams & Co. make these patchwork cushions to co-ordinate with curtains, blinds, quilts, bedcovers, cot-bumpers and head-boards, all of which they can supply by mail order in a customer's choice of fabric. Alphabet cushions cost £13, and cushions with bows cost £15, including p & p. For a catalogue, contact *Adams & Co., Kingston Rd., Bradford-on-Avon, Wilts. BA15 1BD. Tel.: 01225-865744.*

◁ Enjoyed by children and adults alike, Barry Skinner's miniature houses are often exact replicas of someone's house. Barry has made them to order for 18 years, using top-grade birch-faced plywood coupled with a selection of other plywoods, hardwoods and decorative mouldings, according to a client's preferences. Generally, the houses are supplied in a natural wood finish, both inside and out, to be decorated by the owner, but can be provided fully painted, too. Barry can build to any design, period, or stage of completion. As a guide, an unpainted two-up two-down house 40cm wide costs £95. For further information, contact *Barry Skinner, Turnpike Cottage, Traeth, Beddgelert, Gwynedd LL55 4YF. Tel.: 01766-890283.*

▷ Printed to co-ordinate with one another within either a primary (as illustrated) or pastel range, the lively and unusual fabrics, wallpapers, borders and friezes from Poppy Ltd are sold worldwide. The fabrics are 100% cotton; the wallpapers have a wipeable finish. A huge range of soft furnishings, gifts, accessories and clothing are also available, decorated with the same choice of designs, to make a fully co-ordinated child's room. For a catalogue, contact *Poppy Ltd, 44 High St, Yarm, Cleveland TS15 9AE. Tel.: 01642-790000.*

▽ Covered in calico or the fabric of your choice, this sofa is handmade by Sarah-Jane Muir, who specializes in upholstered furniture for children. She also makes armchairs and a range of upholstered accessories, such as waste-paper bins, notice boards, key boards and stools. Her sofas measure approximately 68cm high x 110cm wide x 60cm deep, and cost from £265. Chairs measure approximately 68cm high x 78cm wide x 60cm deep, and start at £210. She also welcomes commissions. *Sarah-Jane Muir Upholstery, Angel Farm, Monks Alley, Binfield, Berks. RG12 5PA. Tel.: 01344-55539.*

△ The Nursery Window stocks not only a wealth of choice in fabrics and wallpapers for young children, with complementary accessories and soft furnishings, but also bedding and matching upholstery for the older child and adult. Refreshing and individual designs are offered, and accessories can be decorated to order. Wallpapers and friezes are coated with a wipeable finish, and fabrics are 100% cotton. For catalogues and more details, contact *The Nursery Window, 83 Walton St, London SW3 2HP. Tel.: 0171-581 3358.*

◁ This Soldier-Soldier bedlinen design is one of several available from Bundles Design Ltd in Liverpool, who specialize in co-ordinating children's fabrics, wallpapers, borders, hand-painted furniture and a myriad of accessories, all available by mail order only. Their bedlinen is made from washable 100% cotton. For mail-order details, contact *Bundles Design Ltd, 222 Century Building, Brunswick Dock, Liverpool L3 4BJ. Tel.: 0151-709 5595.*

Flooring

One of the thorniest decorating problems is what to put on the floor. The vast choice includes parquet, oak, linoleum, slate, stone, terracotta, sisal and rugs.

▽ A parquet wood-block floor in reclaimed Rhodesian teak supplied by The London Architectural Salvage & Supply Co. Ltd, who stock over 30 different types of reclaimed and high-quality hardwood floors. Alternative materials include York stone, terracotta and marble tiles. Its experts source the large, decorative and antique, employing a thorough knowledge of the use and application of anything from an escutcheon to a bronze revolving door. They sell to contractor, connoisseur, exporter and architect alike. For flooring, contact: *LASSCo Antique Flooring Warehouse, Britannia Walk (off City Rd), London N1 7LU. Tel.: 0171-251 5157.*

▷ This beautiful parquet floor of solid prime oak is one of many hardwood floors that Campbell Marson supply. A full range of samples, including bespoke borders and centre pieces, is on display at their showroom. For DIY, most flooring can be purchased at their Wimbledon warehouse: *Campbell Marson & Co. Ltd, 34 Wimbledon Business Centre, Riverside Rd, London SW17 0BA. Tel.: 0181-879 1909. Showroom: 573 Kings Rd, London SW6 2EB. Tel.: 0171-371 5001.*

▷ This top-of-the-range decorative oak-panel floor was supplied by A.R.T. Hardwood Flooring. They stock most solid hardwood flooring, with prices ranging from £65 to £120 per sq. m, and undertake commissions, both commercial and domestic. They lay a floor designed in any pattern – either by a customer or by A.R.T. A repair and restoration service is also available. *A.R.T. Hardwood Flooring, 7 Deans Close, Amersham, Bucks. HP6 6LW. Tel.: 01494-433287.*

▽ Beautifully executed painted floors such as this look stunning and form a focal point. Thomas Lane creates his floors with great attention to detail, working closely with a client, and hand-mixing the colours. For his most basic service – mixing a colour and applying it as a stain – he charges £180. His design prices start at £500 for a simple border in a small room. Contact *Thomas Lane, 57 Wellington Row, London E2 7BB. Tel.: 0171-729 6195.*

△ Finewood Floors Ltd specialize in wide-plank and parquet floors, made from a variety of solid, kiln-dried hardwoods, including oak, maple, ash, cherry, elm, and many others. Their wood is cut into long lengths to produce a distinctive appearance and they can accommodate a wide range of lengths, widths and thicknesses. They also supply custom-made kitchen worktops and tabletops in a choice of solid hardwoods and thicknesses. Visit the showroom at *Finewood Floors Ltd, Unit 5, Gibson Business Centre, (rear of) 800 High Rd, London N17 0DH. Tel.: 0181-365 0222.*

◁ Drawing on a glorious palette of 66 colours, Sinclair Till can cut linoleum to any pattern or lay it as one colour. The effect is gentle and sophisticated or bold and dramatic. Prices start at £17 per sq. m for a plain floor. They also stock a range of hardwood flooring from replenishable sources, starting at £25 per sq. m to supply the wood, or £75 per sq. m to supply and fit, from *Sinclair Till, 791-793 Wandsworth Rd, London SW8 3JQ. Tel.: 0171-720 0031.*

FLOORING

◁ Natural slate has been employed in both this vanity unit and elaborate floor. Burlington Slate also fashion it into kitchen tops, work surfaces, surrounds for mirrors and baths, dado rails, architraves and sills. Providing a selection of standard products, they also produce bespoke work. The vanity unit shown costs £435, before fitting. The London Showroom is at *Burlington Slate, 15 Queen Anne's Gate, London SW1H 9BU. Tel.: 0171-976 7676.*

▽ Paris Ceramics offer a wide range of specialist products and services, as this French limestone floor with tumbled-stone cabochons testifies. Famous for their antique limestone and terracotta, and newly quarried limestone, they also make hand-painted decorative ceramics and stock a broad range of antique floors. Also available: floor tiles, floor mosaics, hand-painted murals and wall tiles. An expert team will design, produce and oversee the installation of one-off floors, murals, mosaics and ceramics. Contact *Paris Ceramics, 583 Kings Rd, London SW6 2EH. Tel.: 0171-371 7778.* Also at *4 Montpellier St, Harrogate, N. Yorks. HG1 2RY. Tel.: 01423-523877.*

▷ Fired Earth (see also pages 144 and 146) stock a wide range of terracotta floor tiles, such as this handmade classic terracotta with a vine border. This material is popular for its warm, variegated colour, its ability to retain warmth and for its extraordinary longevity. Fired Earth also offer slate, limestone and quarry tiles. *Fired Earth, Twyford Mill, Oxford Rd, Adderbury, Oxon OX17 3HP. Tel.: 01295-812088.* See also **Textiles** and **Wallpaper and Paint.**

▽ Natural stone, sourced from the UK, Europe, India and China is imported and supplied by Stonell Ltd. In stock are limestone, sandstone, slate, granite and marble, all in various sizes, styles and colours, many of them exclusive to Stonell. A London showroom has recently opened, where stone can be seen *in situ* as part of a kitchen, or underwater as in a swimming-pool, or incorporated in a shower or vanity unit, or simply laid on the floor in a large area. For a brochure, contact *Stonell Ltd, Unit 1, Bockingfold, Ladham Rd, Goudhurst, Kent TN17 1LY. Tel.: 01580-211167* or visit the showroom: *521/523 Battersea Pk Rd, London SW11 3BN. Tel.: 0171-738 0606.*

△ The beauty and versatility of stone is aptly illustrated by this selection from Stone Age, who are specialists in limestone and sandstone flooring, with the largest range in the UK. The colour is not limited to beige or off-white: with over 30 different stones, each available in a number of finishes and sizes, the possibilities are endless. They also stock fireplaces. Prices start at £53 per sq. m, from *Stone Age Ltd, 19 Filmer Rd, London SW6 7BU. Tel.: 0171-385 7954.*

◁ These runners form part of Roger Oates's new Country Weavers Collection of fine English-made rugs, carpets and furnishings. In 60cm-wide pure new wool, they are available in standard sizes or lengths made to order, at £39 per linear m; just part of an exclusive range of wool, cotton and natural-fibre floor coverings from *Roger Oates Designs, The Long Barn, Eastnor, Ledbury, Hereford, HR8 1EL. Tel.: 01531-632718.*

▷ Hardwearing and practical, yet elegant and natural-looking, these sisal carpets are made by Sans Frontières, in over 20 different designs that are based on natural tones. Their fibres are the best quality available. Sans Frontières also produce sisal screen-printed by machine, in a choice of three designs, and a range of carpet tiles in a mixture of sisal and cocos, which come in two colours – natural and bleached. View in the showroom, by appointment only, or contact their sales office for your local stockist: *Sans Frontières Ltd, 26 Danbury St, London N1 8JU.*

▽ 'Grassroots', by Fired Earth (see also pages 143 and 146), is an exclusive range of woven natural-fibre floor coverings, made from 100% renewable plant fibre. The simple materials of grass, jute, coir and sisal are offered, in classic tones and textures, such as in 'Woodstock', illustrated, to make strong and long-lasting carpeting. This can be laid close-fitted or made up into finished mats by *Fired Earth, Twyford Mill, Oxford Rd, Adderbury, Oxon OX17 3HP. Tel.: 01295-812088.* See also **Textiles** and **Wallpaper and Paint**.

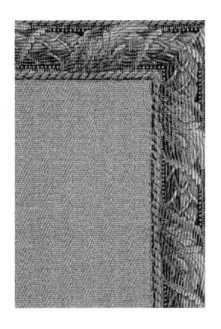

◁ The Carpet Library maintains probably the largest collection of carpet information and sampling in London. A one-stop carpet shop for architects and designers, the library enjoys the backing of all major carpet manufacturers and offers custom-made carpeting to the public. Thousands of colour options are available, plus a huge selection of natural floorcoverings and a broad range of tapestry borders that can be attached to them, making rugs or runners (as illustrated). Every aspect of bespoke carpeting is supplied, with staff on hand to offer advice and prices tailored to suit most budgets. *The Carpet Library Ltd, 148 Wandsworth Bridge Rd, London SW6 2UH. Tel.: 0171-736 3664.*

△ The 'Simply Natural' range of pure wool carpeting in a tufted loop pile, from Tintawn Weaving Co., comes in two designs: Ribgrass (in ten natural colourways, with highlight colours such as lavender and nutmeg) and Grosgrain (in three natural colours only). Various other ranges include pure jutes or combined wool and nylon. Prices start at £30.45 per sq. m, from *Tintawn Weaving Co., The Old Kings Head Court, 11 High St, Dorking, Surrey RH4 1AR. Tel.: 01306-884451.*

▽ Equally at home in both a modern and traditional setting, this attractive rush matting is made entirely by hand from natural fibres, following an age-old craft. Waveney Apple Growers make mats to the requirements of a customer, at £80 per sq. m. They also supply handmade baskets in standard sizes as well as made-to-measure. For a comprehensive catalogue, contact *Waveney Apple Growers Ltd, Common Rd, Aldeby, Suffolk NR34 0BL. Tel.: 01502-677345.*

△ This amusing doormat is hand-stencilled and made from natural coir. Happy Mats offer 15 animal designs in black, bottle green and burgundy, in eight standard sizes or custom-made. Ivy, floral and fleur-de-lis designs are also available, ideal for hall, kitchen or conservatory, from £19. *Happy Mats Ltd, Fair Rigg Cottage, Newby Bridge, Ulverston, Cumbria LA12 8NQ. Tel.: 01768-892525.*

▷ This hand-woven rug by vet-turned-weaver, Alan Foulds, is typical of his strong Scandinavian-influenced contemporary designs. He makes rugs and wall-hangings in a variety of designs and colours to order, using natural yarns: wool, mohair, horsehair and linen. Rug prices start at around £300, from *Alan Foulds, Orchard Cottage, Buskwood, Hope-under-Dinmore, Hereford HR6 0PX. Tel.: 01568-797520.*

▽ Well-known for their stone and stoneware floor tiles, Fired Earth (see also pages 143 and 144) supply a range of tribal rugs, gabbehs (as shown) and kelims. All are handmade by the Kashgai of southern Iran, who maintain the quality and integrity of traditional pieces, uncompromised by modern commercialism and unspoilt by tourism. By specializing in one production outlet, Fired Earth offer expert knowledge and reasonable prices. *Fired Earth, Twyford Mill, Oxford Rd, Adderbury, Oxon OX17 3HP. Tel.: 01295-812088.* See also **Textiles** and **Wallpaper and Paint**.

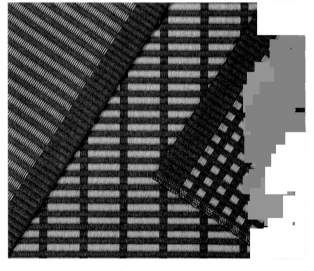

△ Paper twine has been woven to make these pleasing 'Woodnotes' floormats. Derived from wood fibre, the twine is durable, resistant to dirt, dust and moisture, and can be recycled. The mats suit numerous settings, are easy to clean and come in a choice of natural hues and simple designs. For samples, prices and more information, contact *Bruno Triplet, 1/1 Chelsea Harbour Design Centre, London SW10 0XE. Tel.: 0171-795 0395*

Lighting

Lighting a room is a crucial element in interior design. A pleasing atmosphere can be created by clever lighting or destroyed by an unsympathetic glare.

◁ 'Venus 1000' is a lamp in the form of a Venus fly-trap by innovative designer Eryka Isaak. The base is a single block of slate, the main leaf, patinated copper, the upper spiky section, brass, which conceals overlapping coloured glass pieces. These shade the light source, Chainlight, a low voltage system, using seven separate bulbs on a chain. The tip is handblown lead crystal. 'Venus 1000' costs £900 and is available by commission from *Eryka Isaak, 12 Lickey Coppice, Cofton Hackett, Birmingham B45 8PG. Tel.: 0121-445 4559.* (Eryka also makes a range of smaller accessories, priced £10–50.)

▽ Robert Welch works in two distinct yet complementary areas: designing and making handmade silverware and special commissions (mainly in metal), and designing and developing industrial products. Shown below are lamps he has designed for Chad Lighting. The 'Torque' standard and table lamps incorporate twisted square section ironwork, supporting a gold-plated brass tube. The two 'Dryad' table lamps and standard lamp incorporate a spiral cage in wrought iron. The two 'Sparta' table lamps and their pendant companion are finished in bright chromium or antique copper. The 'November' uplighter has a black and chrome finish and gold-plated light spill. Available from *Robert Welch Studio Shops* (which sell only his designs), *Lower High St, Chipping Campden, Glos. GL55 6DY. Tel.: 01386-840522,* and *19 Old Sq., Warwick CV34 4RU. Tel.: 01926-400422.*

▷ The Study offers British-designed contemporary furniture and lighting, by Mark Brazier-Jones, Christopher Neville and Charlotte Packe, among others. The lamps shown right are by Michael Young. 'Mama George' and 'Baby Sessel' are made of nickel-plated brass, their shades hand-woven from stainless-steel cable. From *The Study, 26 Old Church St, London SW3 5BY. Tel.: 0171-376 7969.*

▽ The Pomegranite Sconce below is from McCloud & Co. Made from copper, steel and woodfibre resin, it is shown here in contract gold, but comes in numerous different finishes, including jewellery enamel in vivid colours. McCloud not only boasts an impressive range of lights, but 27 standard finishes and a unique specialized technique of water gilding with 22ct gold on to steel. For prices, contact or visit the showroom of *McCloud & Co. Ltd, 269 Wandsworth Bridge Rd, London SW6 2TX. Tel.: 0171-371 7151.*

△ Chelsea Lighting Design stock a mains-voltage flexible Ropelight (Ref. C040), consisting of miniature lamps sealed inside a silicone tube. Ideal to provide a glow outlining an alcove, as here, or above a window pelmet. It costs about £42.50 per metre from *Chelsea Lighting Design Ltd, Unit 1, 23a Smith St, London SW3 4EJ. Tel.: 0171-824 8144.*

◁ The flawless lines of Clare Thatcher's 'Curvaceous Reading Light' are testimony to her skill in working with glass and metal. Clare designs and makes decorative lights and accessories to commission. Her pieces range from candlesticks to chandeliers. This light costs £250, is adjustable, and the glass shade comes in a variety of colours. Contact *Clare Thatcher Lighting Design, 44 Seymour Rd, Chingford, London E4 7LS. Tel.: 0181-524 0912.*

◁ Peter Wylly's brilliantly coloured and original silk lampshades, with their fluid, organic shapes, are inspired by trips to the East and an interest in the philosophy of balance and harmony. They are all hand-wrapped and designed to create a mood through the magical effect of light and colour. Peter will also create one-off pieces, chandeliers, wall lights, recycled-paper shades and standing lamps. For prices, brochure and recommended stockists, contact *Peter Wylly Lighting, 2nd Floor, Imperial Works, Perren St, London NW5 3ED. Tel.: 0171-267 9598.*

▷ Simon Cahill and Sharon Walker of Unit 9 make refined contemporary furniture, lighting and accessories from a range of materials, including steel, aluminium and glass. Their classic lines sit happily in traditional and modern interiors. The 'Skylon' table lamp (right) is made from chromium-plated mild steel, has a hand-woven natural raffia shade, and costs £60 + p & p. It is available in two sizes and for use as a pendant shade, by mail order from *Unit 9, Shed Eleven Studio, 12 Plumptre Street, The Lace Market, Nottingham NG1 1JL. Tel.: 0115-958 9136.*

▽ This Gothic Lantern is one of a range of handmade lights designed by the Light Brigade to suit farmhouses, cottages and other period homes. Inspired by medieval motifs, the lights have been kept simple, in the spirit of the Arts and Crafts Movement. Available in a selection of woods, antiqued finishes, unpainted or colour-matched, it costs £149.50 (a simplified version is £97.50). *The Light Brigade, 28 Rodney Rd, Cheltenham, Glos. GL50 1JJ. Tel.: 01242-226777.*

◁ This brilliant blue 'Temple' lamp, is part of a collection by Mark Croxford with pleasing, distinctive shapes, designed to enhance any modern living space. Made from plaster or resin, they are hand-finished and come in a range of colours (without shades). Prices start at £77.50. Order from *Mark Croxford Lamps and Interiors, Tel.: 0181-985 1486.*

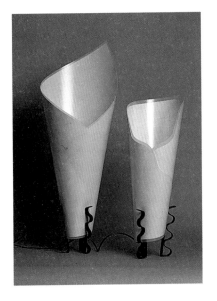

▷ Furniture designer-maker Euan Cunningham's innovative, amusing light has a spun-aluminium shade, steel stand, turned brass detail, copper handle and MDF base. Available in any colour, it is 57cm high, 30cm (max.) wide and can be dismantled. It is not mass produced and costs £100. Euan also accepts commissions. Contact him at *Treve Cottage, River Common, Petworth, W. Sussex GU28 9BH. Tel.: 01798-861257.*

△ The stylish cone-shaped table lamps above have metal bases and laminated parchment shades. They are made by Definitive, a design-craft based company specializing in hand-finished products. Their range includes furniture, lighting, vases and picture frames. They also make one-off commissions. The lamps come in various colours and are available by mail order. Prices start from £65. *Definitive, 37 Catharine St, Liverpool L8 7NE. Tel.: 0151-709 5415.*

▽ Papermaker Joanne Leahy of Strawberry Crafts Co-operative uses natural dyes, such as onion skins, to give her lampshades a warm glow. These lamps, made from reclaimed copper and brass by metal sculptor Neil Walker, cost £98 each. Strawberry Crafts Co-operative also make tables and candlesticks, work to commission and run paper-making and metal workshops. Contact *Strawberry Crafts Co-operative, Beckford Stores, Beckford, Nr Tewkesbury, Glos. GL20 7AD. Tel.: 01386-881248.*

◁ Part of Robert Wyatt's new range, these slim monochrome lampshades are elegant yet quirky. The white shades, decorated with black chenille trim and illustrations from the 1950s, are 30cm high and cost £26. Shades and bases by mail order from *Robert Wyatt Lampshades, 13 The Shrubbery, Grosvenor Rd, Wanstead, London E11 2EL. Tel.: 0181-530 6891.*

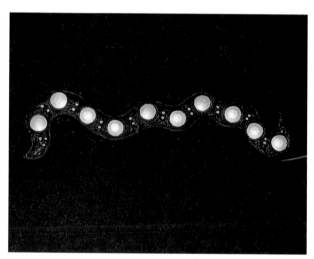

▷ The Protector Lamp & Lighting Company produces a range of replica and modern interpretations of original brass miners' flame lamps. Shown here is an authentic miners' lamp, which is 25cm high and costs £52.35 + p & p, and a half-size non-working miniature brass lamp, which costs £14.53 + p & p. They are available from *The Protector Lamp & Lighting Company, Lansdowne Rd, Eccles, Manchester M30 9PH. Tel.: 0161-789 3013.*

△ Francesca Parsons specializes in designing and making glass and metal lighting. Her avant-garde 'Octopus' wall or corner light is one of a range based on the ocean floor. The light measures 95 x 25cm, is made from copper and glass, and costs £450. Francesca also accepts commissions. Contact her at *2/4 Southgate Rd, London N1 3JJ. Tel.: 0171-923 4446.*

△ A beautiful table lamp, designed and hand-painted by Cressida Bell, with a selection of hand-printed shawls. The current range includes painted lamps, shades, cushions and pots, as well as shawls, scarves and ties. Prices for lamps start at £180; scarves cost £29.50–£112. Cressida Bell also undertakes commissions for carpet, curtain and upholstery designs, painted furniture and complete interiors. *Cressida Bell Ltd, 1a Princeton St, London WC1R 4AX. Tel.: 0171-404 3191* (closed Mon).

◁ For the past ten years Jack Wimperis has been working on commissions in London and the Cotswolds as a stained-glass artist. English antique handblown glass and traditional leading predominate, but he also uses flashed, etched glass, painted kiln-fired glass, sand-blasted frosting and carved leadwork. In his more recent work, he has included stained-glass constructions that incorporate artificial light (see left). For prices, contact *Jack Wimperis, Piccadilly Mill, Lower St, Stroud, Glos. GL5 2HT. Tel.: 01453-764151.*

© Pete Wisbey

▷ Hugh St. Clair has put a pineapple to practical use to create this striking 'Ananas' lamp, made from woven steel. Middle Eastern towers, French bowling balls and sunflowers have inspired other lamps of gilded wood, polished mahogany or silver. Included in his range is the steel 'Boscage' table and 'Jonah', a stainless-steel and glass bathroom storage system. This lamp is 48cm in height x 45cm at its widest. The base costs £150, the shade, £35; both available from *Hugh St. Clair Designs, 5 Fish Hill, Holt, Norfolk N25 6BD. Tel.: 01263-713551.*

△ A range of Patrick Quigly's stylish contemporary designs shows table lamps in dark faux-parchment. They are also available in light faux-parchment, crushed velvet and fake fur. Patrick sells wall lights, pendants and a comprehensive collection of cone, coolie and empire-style shades to fit every light, from chandeliers to large table and floor lamps. Shades cost from £19; table lamps and wall lights, from £39. Contact *Patrick Quigly, 7–9 Earlham St, London WC2H 9LL. Tel.: 0171-240 8001.*

▽ This attractive 'real rust' pineapple chandelier with a verdigris finish is part of a range from the Monica Pitman Collection, which comprises lighting, metal furniture and decorative objects inspired by 18th and 19thC antiques (see also **Tables and Chairs** and **Decorative Accessories**). The light is available to order in different finishes and costs £451. Visit the showroom, which is open Mon–Fri 9.30am–5pm, or contact *The Monica Pitman Collection, M5 Chelsea Garden Market, Chelsea Harbour, London SW10 0XE. Tel.: 0171-376 3180.*

△ Catherine Purves's delicate Oak Leaf wall light is made from welded steel, brass-plated and patinated for a weathered effect. The fitting is behind the leaf, which reflects the light on to the wall. It measures 60 x 30cm and costs £98. Contact *Catherine Purves, Divine Lights, 20 Steward St, London E1 6AJ. Tel.: 0171-247 1938.*

Decorative Fixtures

Gone are the old stainless-steel door handles and coat hooks and the plastic curtain tracks. Fixtures and fittings are now made with style in a multitude of different materials from porcelain to patinated copper.

These beautifully
worked curtain poles
and finials are
produced by The
Bradley Collection,
who are specialists in
designing and
making tassels and
accessories in a
selection of materials
and finishes, to
include traditionally
forged steel, carved
wood and hand-
painted decoration.
*The Bradley
Collection Ltd, The
Granary, Flowton
Brook, Flowton,
Suffolk IP8 4LJ.
Tel.: 01473-652651.*

DECORATIVE FIXTURES

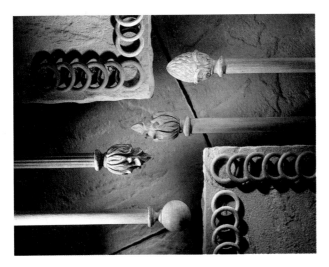

◁ The Craft Pole collection offers rustic Mediterranean charm, with three different finials and a choice of finishes. Only timber from sustainable sources only is used and prices start at £34.99 per 1.2m. Other hand-crafted collections offer wrought-iron, antique brass and wood effects, and tie-backs, hold-backs and draw rods; all sold in leading DIY superstores and other outlets. For more information, contact *Harrison Drape, Bradford St, Birmingham B12 0PE. Tel.: 0121-766 6111.*

▽ Exclusive designs in a multitude of finishes are on offer from Cope & Timmins Ltd, in their range of made-to-measure curtain poles and finials, fashioned from wrought-iron, brass, and wood. Price range for finials: £6.50-112.50 per pair. Poles: £8.95-86.50 per m. Also supplied is a huge choice of other accessories for window-furnishing, soft-furnishing and the bathroom, as well as much more. For a brochure and local stockists, contact *Cope & Timmins Ltd., Angel Rd Works, Angel Rd, Edmonton, London N18 3AY. Tel.: 0181-803 6481.*

△ Luxury curtain rods and accessories in a myriad of styles and finishes, such as these wrought-iron examples, are available from Varia Textiles. As well as highly decorative and detailed rods in iron, brass and carved wood, they stock a huge selection of high-quality accessories such as tie-backs, carved bed canopies, and door furniture. The curtain rods illustrated range from £150 to £255. For brochures, contact *Varia Textiles, 197 Kings Rd, Kingston-upon-Thames, Surrey KT2 5JH. Tel.: 0181-549 8590.*

DECORATIVE FIXTURES

▷ These attractive curtain clips (also made with square rings) come in a choice of finishes: antique brass, pewter or black. Simply sew up a handkerchief of curtain fabric and clip it straight on to a thin pole. The clips measure 25 or 37mm and cost £3.20 each + p & p Also available is a range of steel rods with cast-metal finials, and other drapery accessories, from *Cambridge Home Fashions, Unit 36, Dry Drayton Industries, Scotland Rd, Dry Drayton, Cambridge CB3 8AT. Tel.: 01954-211931.*

◁ Jane Cooper Designs supply a number of decorative fittings, mainly made from brass that is hot-stamped, hand-buffed to an 'antique' finish, and finally lacquered. Their range covers hooks (as illustrated), curtain tie-backs, hold-backs and cleats. They also make candlesticks, sconces and an over-the-bath sconce that can hold a wine glass. Hooks start at £5.50. For a brochure, contact *Jane Cooper Designs, 30 Friern Park, London N12 9DA. Tel.: 0181-446 8595.*

DECORATIVE FIXTURES

◁ The Archive collection consists of finely worked traditional designs for finials and hold-backs, with more innovative styles for swag-holders and sew-on decorations. A range of themes includes: red-and-gilt heraldic; richly coloured floral and sunblast; abundant fruits; seashore; and nursery. Rich in detail and eye-catching, all accessories are hand-painted to create distinctive and original decoration. Finials start from £39 per pair. For a brochure, contact *Hang-Ups Accessories Ltd, Unit 7, Lyncroft Farm Workshops, Perrotts Brook, Cirencester, Glos. GL7 7BW. Tel.: 01285-831771.*

▷ The Felbrigg Design Company (see also **Screens**) specializes in fine interior decoration and produces a number of decorative items, such as these gesso copies of Florentine tassels. Painted to imitate wood, they can be supplied with flat backs so that they lie flush against a wall or pelmet and cost £14.95. They can also be painted to match any scheme, and are sold with a co-ordinating rope. Lamps and shades, footstools, waste bins, urns, cushions and much more are also available. *The Felbrigg Design Company, The Coach House, 4 Park La., Sutton Benger, Wilts. SN15 4RN. Tel.: 01249-720076.*

▷ Resina Designs focus attention on design, colour and detail to create decorative and affordable window treatments. Every item is made and finished by hand, employing the best traditional and modern techniques. They offer a varied range of finials, an established stock of accessories, and a bespoke service, matching any colour. *Resina Designs, Unit 6a, Burnett Industrial Estate, Wrington, Bristol BS18 7QU. Tel.: 01934-863535.*

◁ The Celtic range of door furniture, made from intricately turned steel, is hand-forged to create a unique basket-weave design, finished in black or patine. An anti-corrosive coating allows for indoor and outdoor use. Clayton Munroe also produce a broad variety of other door and cabinet fittings, finely worked in numerous metals and finishes. A Celtic lever handle set costs £52.30. For a brochure, get in touch with *Clayton Munroe Ltd, Kingston, Staverton, Totnes, Devon TQ9 6AR. Tel.: 01803-762626.*

▷ Stephen Roberts produces durable door furniture entirely made, cast and finished by hand from reconstituted stone. His door knobs, back-plates and escutcheons come in five finishes and a host of exquisite designs, such as the heads of pelicans; a lotus bud; and seashells, to mention but a few. His cabinet knobs double as pegs, and each piece fits comfortably in the hand. For both internal and external use. Door knobs start at £35 per pair; cabinet knobs at £6 each. Stephen also makes bathroom accessories. *Turnstyle Designs, 1 Bridge Chambers, The Square, Barnstaple, Devon EX31 1HB. Tel.: 01271-25325.*

▽ Handmade from porcelain and carefully decorated, these cupboard and drawer pulls come in three designs: shell, ammonite and scroll. Various finishes complement both natural wood and painted surfaces, and include 22ct gold leaf. Sizes range from 30 to 45mm; prices from £8.50 to £14 each. Julie also makes other accessories and hand-painted tiles (see **Tiles**). *Julie Arnall, 26 Woodwaye, Watford, Herts. WD1 4NW. Tel.: 01923-228465.*

△ Solid, weighty and tactile, these luxurious furniture handles are hand-cast in solid brass and bronze, using the lost-wax process, and with five different finishes applied by hand, among them polished, verdigris and patinated. A wide range of designs is available, apart from those illustrated. Sizes range from 25 to 55mm wide, with prices from £14 each. *Ornamental Arts Trading Ltd, Unit 1-7, Chelsea Harbour Design Centre, Chelsea Harbour, London SW10 0XE. Tel.: 0171-385 4304.*

◁ A once-forgotten and newly found set of original patterns – Victorian, Edwardian and art deco – have been used to make a huge and exciting range of door furniture. Each piece in the 'Rawnsley Products' collection is hand-cast in iron by traditional methods and hand-finished with a resin paint to ensure durability and echo the original effect. The hooks illustrated range from £6.90 to £11.90 per pair. Contact *Joseph Tipper Ltd, Century Works, Moat St, Willenhall, W. Midlands WV13 1FZ. Tel.: 01902-608444.*

◁ Elaine Banks makes these 'Wiggle' door handles in a choice of metals (shown here in pewter) and sizes, from £125 per pair. Elaine designs and makes a broad range of elegant, fluid and tactile furniture and accessories, including towel rails, hooks and candle sconces. As well as developing and selling established ranges, she works to commission. *Elaine Banks, 91 Brook Drive, London SE11 4TU. Tel.: 0171-582 1156.*

▽ James Cox designs and makes a variety of door handles inspired by the sea. With use, the patinated copper finish gradually burnishes, so enhancing their appearance. Door handles cost £156 a pair; cupboard knobs £26 each. Contact *James Cox at Tin Star Studio, 38 Cheltenham Place, Brighton, E. Sussex BN1 4AB. Tel.: 01273-606289.*

Wall Coverings

*Specialist paints and wallpapers recreate the colours and designs of the past.
Like wallpapers, paint effects – stencilling, stamping and* trompe l'œil *– give
a feeling of depth and texture to your walls.*

▷ The result of considerable research and development with the Victoria and Albert Museum, the Fired Earth Historic Paint Range presents a fascinating palette of authentic 18th and 19thC colours. These are available in the traditional finishes of flat oil and distemper, as well as eggshell and emulsion. Prices range from £15.50 to £18.75 for 2.5 litres and sample tins of emulsion (100ml) cost £2.50. See also **Textiles** and **Flooring**. *Fired Earth, Twyford Mill, Oxford Rd, Adderbury, Oxon OX17 3HP. Tel.: 01295-812088.*

▽ A small wallpaper company in Gloucester, Alexander Beauchamp specializes in reproducing historical papers by means of screen-printing, which ensures excellent quality, colour and texture. Among their best sellers are traditional damask patterns that imitate 16thC silks, but they also produce whimsical designs and sell to customers all over the world. *Alexander Beauchamp, Vulcan Hse, Stratton Rd, Gloucester GL1 4HL. Tel.: 01452-384959.*

△ This specially hand-printed wallpaper, Royal Crescent is available to order in any colourway and based on an original fragment dating from c.1775. Hamilton Weston reproduce designs from old fragments for private commissions or for museums and restoration work. Some are available to the public, either as hand or machine prints, at their retail shop, where they hold a large selection of wallpapers, borders, fabrics, trimmings and accessories from unusual sources. An interior design service is also offered. *Hamilton Weston Wallpapers Ltd, 18 St. Mary's Grove, Richmond, Surrey TW9 1UY. Tel.: 0181-940 4850.*

◁ This Bathtime design by Cath Kidston, shown here as wallpaper, comes in five colourways at £23.50 a roll. It is also available in 100% cotton fabric and cotton towelling, accompanied by a range of co-ordinating bathroom accessories. Other wallpaper designs offered are Rose Bouquet (a classic, big rose print in seven colourways; £23.50 a roll) and Fern Leaf (a simple design in five colourways; about £17.60 a roll). This shop also sells painted furniture, bedlinen and various household items. *Cath Kidston, 8 Clarendon Cross, London W11 4AP. Tel.: 0171-221 4000.*

▽ This simple *trompe-l'œil* niche by Niggy Thomas (see also **Tables and Chairs** and **Cupboards and Chests**) provides relief on an otherwise boring expanse of wall. Niggy also hand-paints individual designs on floors (he has created, for example, a 3 x 1.65m 'kilim') and hand-paints furniture. Both ideas make unusual personalized presents. Prices start at around £75, depending on the size and complexity of the work. *Niggy Thomas, 18 Ashmount Rd, London N19 3BJ. Tel.: 0171-272 6078 or 01625-525205.*

◁ With its lavish gold decoration, this wall cupboard is typical of Angela Beaumont's approach to period detail. She supplies custom-made decorated furniture, often employing gilding and crackle-glaze techniques, to a wide variety of commissions for walls and furniture, many of them involving extremely complicated work. She also runs stencilling courses. This cupboard measures 90cm high x 45cm wide, can be custom-made, and costs £270, from *Angela Beaumont, 12-14 Hainworth Village, Keighley, W. Yorks. BD21 5QH. Tel.: 0153-5604381.*

▷ This delightful 'grow-your-own cherry tree' stencil is only one example of more than a thousand stencils designed by The Stencil Library. It costs £31.50 to buy, or £15.75 for one month's hire. Stencil supplies, day courses, designing, cutting and stencilling courses are also available. For more information, contact *The Stencil Library, Stocksfield Hall, Stocksfield, Northumb. NE43 7TN. Tel.: 01661-844844.*

▽ A host of versatile and lively stamps are supplied by First Class Stamps, by mail order. Their series of Decorstamps is continuously being developed and currently contains such themes as Beatrix Potter characters, animals (wild and farm), fish and plantlife, and more. The designs can be applied with ink pads, fabric inks, embossing powder or water-based paint on to wood, fabric, paper and unglazed ceramics. Prices start at £3.50 for an individual stamp; packs are also available. For a brochure, contact *First Class Stamps Ltd, Hall Staithe, Fakenham, Norfolk NR21 9BW. Tel.: 01328-851449.*

△ Eleanor Allitt designs and makes high-quality and original stencils. They are made from a plastic film that is light and adheres easily to any surface, and many come in large sizes for ease and speed. They start at £4.80. Her comprehensive service includes all the materials you need, plus an instruction video; also workshops and demonstrations. *Eleanor Allitt, Thickthorn Cottage, 108 Leamington Rd, Kenilworth, Warwickshire CV8 2AA. Tel.: 01926-52395.*

◁ Perfect for period homes, the stencils supplied by The Lansdowne Collection are re-editions of authentic designs, most of them dating from the mid 19thC to the 1930s. This small company not only sells stencils at a starting price of £9.95 but also works to private and public commissions, including The National Trust, and runs one- and two-day stencilling courses, starting at £35. *The Lansdowne Collection, 35 Lansdowne Crescent, Glasgow G20 6NH. Tel.: 0141-339 6546.*

PAINT EFFECTS

© Gerald Corbett

▷ Providing stamps to suit most tastes, The English Stamp Company offers numerous themes, with stamps measuring either 2in. (5cm) at £6.95 or 4in. (10cm) at £12.95. Also offered are paints and rollers, complete stamp kits, Christmas-stamp kits, and others for achieving an antique-paint finish. Stamps can also be made to order in a customer's design. For mail-order details, contact *The English Stamp Company, Sunnydown, Worth Matravers, Dorset BH19 3JP. Tel.: 01929-439117.*

△ Over 150 stencil designs, from Mini Stencils (10cm sq.; £2.75 each) to large Premier Stencils, such as this fruit chalice, about 40cm sq. (£10.95-17.95 each), are designed and supplied by The Painted Finish. Also a useful range of accessories: paints, brushes, stencil film, glazes, varnishes and other specialist tools. Their workshops begin with basic stencilling and continue to more advanced techniques. To find a local stockist, contact *The Painted Finish, Unit 6, Hatton Country World, Hatton, Warwick CV35 8XA. Tel.: 01926-842376.*

△ The Stamping Ground offers 40 stamp designs, for use on walls, fabrics, picture frames, and so on. Themes include Gothic, Baroque, country, marine and nursery. The stamps are well made from red rubber on a beech base, and measure 7.5cm (for £8.95) or 12.5cm (for £10.95). Rollers and gold paint (as illustrated) are also supplied. For a free brochure, contact *The Stamping Ground, PO Box 1364, London W5 5ZH. Tel.: 0181-758 8629.*

The Garden

Whether you have rolling acres in the heart of the country or a pocket handkerchief in the centre of town, the furniture, pots, urns, trugs and other functional and decorative accessories here should strike many a chord.

◁ Ideal for incorporation as garden features, fireplace ornament, or typically decorating façades of buildings, many of the designs available from the Bulmer Brick & Tile Company (some of which are shown here) are made in moulds that are over 100 years old. Their inspiration was very much part of the 19thC Gothic revival, drawing on classical subjects and motifs. More recent moulds reflect the need for conservation and restoration and a renewed interest in classical design. Contact *Bulmer Brick & Tile Co. Ltd, The Brickfields, Bulmer, Sudbury, Suffolk CO10 7EF. Tel.: 01787-269232.*

▷ Whichford Pottery produce an impressive selection of handmade terracotta pots in a variety of sizes and designs. They also make traditional horticultural ware, such as long toms, alpine pans, rhubarb and seakale forcers. Every pot is stamped with the year of manufacture, carries a ten-year guarantee against frost damage, and mellows beautifully with age. Visitors to the Pottery can see the pots being made. Outside, an immense number of pots are on display, many of them planted to show their effectiveness in the garden. A nationwide delivery service is available. For a catalogue, please send six first-class stamps to *Whichford Pottery, Whichford, Nr Shipston-on-Stour, Warwickshire CV36 5PG. Tel.: 01608-684416.* See also **Tiles**.

▷ Jane Hogben launched her collection of decorative terracotta for the house and garden in 1991. Attractive pots and bowls, sprigged with cockerel, daisy, fleur-de-lis, cherub and seahorse designs, together with animal sculptures of pigs, hens, ducks and birds, comprise the range. Each piece is hand-modelled; Jane also undertakes commissions. For further information, contact *Jane Hogben Ceramics, Grove House, East Common, Gerrards Cross, Bucks. SL9 7AF. Tel.: 01753-882364.*

▽ These award-winning rope-covered pots use honey-brown ship's ropes with traditional sailor's knots. They are long lasting, mellow with age and, with their story – seafarers used to make miniature versions in fishing twine as keepsakes for their sweethearts – make the perfect addition to a romantic garden. Three sizes are available. Prices are from £25 for a 29cm-diameter pot. Rope swings, sea chest and bollard seats, hanging tables and hammocks are included in the range. Contact *The Garden Ropework Company, 47 West Hill, Hitchin, Herts. SG5 2HY. Tel.: 01462-456553.*

△ Kemptown Terracotta produce an ever increasing range of garden pots from a local Sussex clay, used to make terracotta for centuries. It fires to a glowing orange and ensures a robust pot, guaranteed against frost damage for ten years. Many of the pots are glazed with a vibrant green rim, the pottery's hallmark. Jugs, bowls and bread bins are among the other items available. Visit the workshop (10am–5.30pm Mon–Sat; please phone first) or contact *Kemptown Terracotta, 5 Arundel Rd, Brighton, E. Sussex BN2 5TE. Tel.: 01273-676603.*

◁ The yard at Hare Lane Pottery is crammed with terracotta pots: long toms, alpine pans, half pots, wall pots and a huge selection of planters. Jonathan Garratt makes them all by hand, using clay from a local pit and firing his big round wood kiln eight times a year. Woodfiring gives the pots a mellow, antique appearance. All pots are guaranteed against frost damage, and prices start at £3.50. Jonathan also makes colourful domestic pots. *Hare Lane Pottery, Cranborne, Wimborne, Dorset BH21 5QT. Tel.: 01725-517700.*

▷ Specialists in English lead statuary, the Bulbeck Foundry boast that they can make anything out of lead, if not precluded through cost or time. They undertake commissions and will incorporate dates, inscriptions and heraldic devices. This Large Adam Urn, a replica of an 18thC original, costs £620, and is part of a range of fountains, birdbaths, herons, planters, statues, cisterns and wall plaques. Bulbeck also have an excellent reputation for the restoration of old leadwork. *The Bulbeck Foundry, Reach Rd, Burwell, Cambs. CB5 0AH. Tel.: 01638-743153.*

▽ Home horticulture is much more attractive with Frolics of Winchester's handmade Grow-Box, designed to take a standard Grow-bag. It comes in various designs and colours: Tsunami (pictured), Humps, Swoops and Brackets, in conifer green, red, white, azure blue, Aztec yellow, or white undercoat for you to decorate. Special designs are available on request. It costs £39.95 + £10 p & p. To order, send a cheque for £49.95; for further details, send an s.a.e. to '*Grow-Box*', *Frolics of Winchester, 82 Canon St, Winchester, Hants. SO23 9JQ. Tel.: 01962-856384.*

△ A practical, elegant solution to the problem of giving your plants constant attention is offered by the St. James self-watering window box from Les Amis du Jardin. Available in four sizes and colours: black, white, dark and light green, the box contains a built-in reservoir that can last several weeks. Removable inner liners lift out so that you can change plantings without moving the box. Prices start at £126.95 excluding delivery. *Les Amis du Jardin, 187 Sussex Gdns, London W2 2RH. Tel.: 0171-262 9141.*

◁ The magnificent reconstituted stone Wedhampton Basin is 1m in diameter and available in Bath or Portland stone finishes, with or without handles. It costs £750 + VAT from the Landscape Ornament Company, whose high-quality range of garden ornaments includes terracotta pots, wooden benches and stone fountains. Priorities are good design and satisfying customers who are looking for something out of the ordinary. *Landscape Ornament Company Ltd, Long Barn, Patney, Devizes, Wilts. SN10 3RB. Tel.: 01380-840533.*

THE GARDEN

▽ Garden designer Anthony de Grey started designing trellis-work when he could not find a style he liked at a reasonable price. His company now produces a range of products from trellis panels and rose arches to arbours, seats and gazebos. The Camer Rose Arch, below, is 2.48m high x 1.22m wide x 61cm deep and costs £445 + VAT and delivery. The side panels are available in diamonds (as shown) or squares (£430 + VAT and delivery). From *Anthony de Grey Trellises, Broadhinton Yard, 77a North St, London SW4 0HQ. Tel.: 0171-738 8866.*

◁ The graceful cast-iron Victoria Arch from HMP, specialists in reconstructing and adapting antique iron garden furniture and structures, as well as recreating classic designs from the past. Benches, tables, bridges, gazebos, staircases, gates and railings number among their other designs. The Victoria Arch costs £425 from *HMP Ltd, Ditchford Farm, Moreton-in-Marsh, Glos. GL56 9RD. Tel.: 01608-662348.*

▷ Maggy Howarth has revived and refined the traditional crafts of cobbling and pebble mosaic, creating intricate designs, glorious patterns and figurative motifs in water-worn natural pebbles of many shapes and sizes. She takes great care in choosing the colours and textures appropriate to the character of the setting. To meet modern needs, most designs are supplied in pre-cast slabs. Maggy only works to commission, and enjoys challenging themes and design problems. She charges £600 per sq. m plus design and installation costs. *Cobblestone Designs, Hilltop, Wennington, Lancaster LA2 8NY. Tel.: 015242-74264.*

△ Timber decking is an original solution to many garden surfacing problems – it is versatile, easy to install, practical, and suits almost any setting. Leisuredeck specialize in designing and installing decking. They use Canadian western red cedar, a timber known for its strength, uniform appearance and weather resistance. The deck shown creates a convenient outdoor living area next to a swimming pool. *Leisuredeck Ltd, Maylands House, Maylands Ave., Hemel Hempstead, Herts. HP2 7DE. Tel.: 01442-242700.*

▷ Graceful curves are the feature of this handsome garden seat from the workshop of wrought-iron furniture designer and maker Mark Francis (see **Tables and Chairs**). It forms part of a range, which includes two- and three-seater benches and tables in the same style, and can be used in the house as well as the garden. Prices range from £300 to £700. Mark is also happy to accept commissions. Contact him by letter or phone, or visit his showroom at *New Street House, New St, Petworth, W. Sussex GU28 0AS. Tel.: 01798-343943.*

▽ The elegant lines of Kettler's Caprice range from their Royal Garden Furniture collection belie its durability. Handmade in wrought-iron and finished in gun-metal grey, the chairs have lattice seats and backs, incorporating delicate hand-crafted scrolls and finely detailed leaves. Prices start at £399 (without cushions). Kettler also distribute garden furniture in resin, steel and wood. For local stockists, contact *Kettler (GB) Ltd, Kettler House, Merse Rd, North Moons Moat, Redditch, Worcs. B98 9HL. Tel.: 01527-591901.*

△ A striking red metal stool by architect turned furniture designer Lucy Fielden. Lucy designs one-off pieces of furniture to commission, and works in wood, metal and glass. In 1988 she designed the Shropshire Set, a simple, elegant range of garden-conservatory furniture in oak. She also produces decorative garden gates. The stool illustrated costs £219 from *Lucy Fielden, Tel.: 0171-259 5108.* See also **Mirrors**.

◁ The pretty 'Victorian Cottage Garden Chair' in wood and iron, copied from an original and available from Carolyn Stephenson (see also p. 184). Shown in Agatha pink, it can be painted in any colour you choose. The chair is part of a set that includes a two- or three-seater bench and table. Treated to withstand the elements, it can be kept in the garden. The chair costs £145 from *Carolyn Stephenson, 96 Tyneham Rd, London SW11 5XP. Tel.: 0171-585 3536.*

▷ A strong, comfortable, but above all extremely elegant garden bench. Sensitively designed and hand-forged in mild steel, it is finished in a durable matt black powder coating to ensure that it can be left outside in all weathers. The bench measures 105cm high x 35cm wide x 145cm long, and costs £950 from *Cara Frost, Claycastle Cottage, South Perrott, Beaminster, Dorset DT8 3HU. Tel.: 01935-891348.*

◁ Every item of furniture created by Silas Birtwistle and Leo Zinovieff is unique. On a commission basis, they make outdoor and indoor benches, chairs and tables from driftwood, which appeals to them because it has been gnarled and bleached by the sea, and the shape of each piece is so unpredictable. They comb beaches for promising pieces of driftwood, and enjoy the challenge of fashioning them into furniture. Prices start at around £500. Silas and Leo also make rush-seated chairs for indoor use. *Silas Birtwistle and Leo Zinovieff, The Stableyard, Coleshill, Nr Faringdon, Oxon SN7 7NB,* or *Tel.: 0181-941 7635.*

◁ Paul Anderson's fascination for primitive, crudely made furniture is evident in his 'Bench for a Mossy Grove', left. Drawn to bits of wood with visible histories, he makes huge solid sculptural chairs, thrones and benches from old oak joists, gates and fences. Paul's intention is that each of his pieces should have a spirit of its own, a strong presence which has elemental beauty. Paul works to commission, and can be contacted at *104 West St, Hartland, Devon EX39 6BQ. Tel.: 01237-441645.*

▷ Furniture designers and makers Gaze Burvill are committed to good design, personal service and superior craftsmanship. They respect the traditions of English garden furniture, crafting limited-edition pieces, whose graceful lines are in harmony with the landscape. This 'May Throne', made of oak from sustainable woodlands, has a comfortable curved back and generous arms, perfect for a glass or book. Gaze Burvill also make tables and benches, and accept special commissions. Prices start at £345 for a low table. *Gaze Burvill, Plain Farm, Old Dairy, East Tisted, Hants. GU34 3RT. Tel.: 01420-587467.*

▽ The Beaulieu Bench and Leagrave Chair, made from the highest-quality teak from sustainable forests in Vietnam, and part of Julian Chichester's garden furniture range. Selected from 18th and 19thC pattern books and the designs of such masters as Chippendale and Hepplewhite, the collection combines decorative styles with solid proportions. Teak furniture can be left outside in any weather. Untreated, it turns silver, or the original colour can be retained with an annual coating of teak oil. For prices and further details, contact *Julian Chichester Designs Ltd, 27 Parsons Green La., London SW6 4HH. Tel.: 0171-371 9055.*

◁ Solid and built to last, with a hint of art nouveau in the decorative slats, high back and lines of the apron, the Milford Seat is based on an Edwardian model. Each bench is handmade from reclaimed oak by Yorkshire carpenter John Ives, using traditional methods: all the joints are pegged, each piece is carved and polished by hand and every seat is numbered and signed. Priced at £500, it can be ordered from *Duncan H. McLaren Ltd, 10 St. James's Pl., London SW1A 1NP. Tel.: 0171-409 0479.*

◁ Comfortable and elegant, the Edwardian Steamer Chair has a robust beech frame with wide arms and a brass drinks holder, which swings out when required. The chair and canopy are adjustable and the extra-long leg rest is removable. The frame is hand rubbed to give a mellow tone. Sarah Burgoyne Revivals also produce a lightweight Terrace Chair and Hammock Bed. All their products can be folded easily. For prices and further details, contact *Sarah Burgoyne Revivals, Whyly, East Hoathly, E. Sussex BN8 6EL. Tel.: 01825-840738.*

▽ Large Palladio umbrellas – the type traditionally used to shade Italian market stalls – and the Lechlade swing seat from Rusco's range of garden furniture. John and Elsa Taylor run the business from their Cotswolds mill house. Tables and chairs, umbrellas and hammocks dominate the collection, which includes a range based on French restaurant furniture, Bandstand, more suitable for small gardens, a selection of wrought-iron furniture from Alabama and traditional teak pieces from Indonesia. The umbrellas come in ten sizes, ranging from 2.5 to 5m in diameter; prices start at £120. The swing seat costs £775 (prices include delivery). Contact *Rusco Marketing, Little Faringdon Mill, Lechlade, Glos. GL7 3QQ. Tel.: 01367-252754.*

The Indian Ocean Trading Company's extensive garden furniture collection features both classics from past ages and contemporary designs. Comfortable, elegant and demonstrating quality craftsmanship, it is built in teak, the most durable hardwood, which, if left outdoors, will mature to a fine silver grey. The large picture shows the Wentworth Oval Table (£950), which can accommodate six to eight in its closed position and up to 12 when fully extended. It is shown with Richmond Recliners (£295 each) and a Cotswold Parasol (360cm; £350). Below right is the Kendal Square Table (£115) and two York Steamers (£350 each), a sleek folding design derived from early liner chairs. The back has three reclining positions and the footstool is removable. The Heavy York Steamer (£450), below left, is slightly larger and made from thicker-gauge timber. Designed for sheer comfort, the back has four reclining positions. Contact *Indian Ocean Trading Company, 28 Ravenswood Rd, London SW12 9PJ. Tel.: 0181-675 4808*, or visit their showroom there.

▽ Designed for a conservatory or garden room, the elegant, distressed-painted Griffin Bench from L'Art du Bois is an exact copy of a 19thC Scottish original. L'Art du Bois produce a comprehensive range of hand-crafted country wooden and painted furniture, and as each piece is individually made, commissioned orders can be accommodated easily. For prices and further information, contact *L'Art du Bois Ltd, Uphampton House, Shobdon, Nr Leominster, Hereford HR6 9PA. Tel.: 01568-708489.*

△ Inspired by the curves of a yacht, the Tredrossel Range by Crafted Comfort Furniture Design consists of tables and chairs, beds, desks, conservatory/garden furniture and planters. The designs are simple, the lines clean, and every piece is made by skilled craftsmen, using timber from sustainable woodlands. The laminated curved frame is made from cherry, which produces durable, lightweight furniture. Strong, flexible and with lovely grain patterns, ash is used for the seat slats. Cushions are optional extras. As shown, the Lynher Seat (three-seater) costs £1,250; the Sheviock Rocker £340; the Tredossel Chair £300 fixed, and £390 folding (prices include packaging but not delivery) from *Crafted Comfort Furniture Design, Tredrossel House, Sheviock, Nr Torpoint, Cornwall PL11 3DZ. Tel.: 01503-30656.*

THE CONSERVATORY AND GARDEN

▷ For indoor and outdoor use, the armchair and two footstools/side tables, pictured here, are from Steamer Furniture's collection of handmade folding wood furniture. Available in the finest seasoned teak from sustainable managed sources or English elm with cherry, the armchair costs £320 in teak and £260 in elm with cherry; the footstool/side table costs £111 in teak and £90 in elm with cherry, from *Steamer Furniture, The Forge, Wigmore, Leominster, Hereford HR6 9UA. Tel.: 01568-770462.*

▽ Trugs have been made in Sussex since Anglo-Saxon times, but in the 1820s Thomas Smith of Herstmonceux brought out a new design – the now familiar basket shape. It was an instant success. Today, the South Down range, below, is made from Finnish birch aircraft plywood, which is durable and weather resistant. The trugs come in a range of sizes and the handles and rims in a choice of colours. For prices and further details, contact *Sussex Trugs Ltd, Thomas Smith's Trug Shop, Hailsham Rd, Herstmonceux, E. Sussex BN27 4LH. Tel.: 01323-832137/833801.*

△ The classic Somerset Trug, in three sizes, large, small and mini, for use in gardens and interiors. Designed and made in Somerset from distress-painted timber, they are available by mail order from Somerset Creative Products, whose range includes rakes, brooms, planters, trays, shelves, herb and candle boxes, and food and egg larders (see **Kitchen Accessories**). Prices for the trugs are £27.50, £32 and £37 + p & p. For further information and mail-order catalogue contact *Somerset Creative Products, Charlecote, Mark, Somerset TA9 4PX. Tel.: 01278-641622.*

◁ An aesthetically pleasing, versatile and durable container, the Robusta Box was originally designed as a log box, but can have a host of different uses. The sides are made from a single larch board (sustainably grown in North Yorkshire), bent into shape employing the same technique that joiners use to put the shoulder bends into coffins. The base board is a concession to the 20thC, being plywood. It costs £30 + £7.50 p & p. To order, telephone *Keith Mott, 2 Chapel Row, Aldfield, Ripon, N. Yorks. HG4 3BG. Tel.: 01765-620306.*

In the heart of rural Kent, Rod Fender designs and produces a great variety of metal artwork at the Black Forge Art workshop. Combining skilful metalwork with artistry, he makes an impressive range of weathervanes, from witches to windsurfers. They are substantial constructions with a large scrolled mounting bracket to fit any vertical surface. Each silhouette starts as a stencil, designed by Rod, then cut freehand from steel and coated in weatherproof satin black finish. As these two illustrations demonstrate, weathervane designs can be made into attractive and original house names with the addition of hand-cut letters, or into decorative wall plaques. Plant hangers, garden ornaments, doorstops, bookends and hooks for keys and dog leads are also available. Commissions for larger one-off designs are happily undertaken. Prices start at £145 for a weathervane, and £75 + £4 per letter for house names. A mail order service is available from *Black Forge Art, Owley Farm, Wittersham, Isle of Oxney, Kent TN30 7HJ. Tel.: 01797-270073.*

THE GARDEN

◁ Reminiscent of an Amish chapel, this galvanized steel bird house is one of a range of four designs from Terrace & Garden, suppliers of decorative garden accessories. They include sundials, signs and markers, weathervanes, lamps, taps in the shape of various animals, watering cans and florist vases. The bird house costs £30 + p & p and is available by mail order from *Terrace & Garden Ltd, Orchard House, Patmore End, Ugley, Bishop's Stortford, Herts. CM22 6JA. Tel.: 01799-543289.*

△ Simon Percival creates functional garden centrepieces in a variety of materials, including stone and metal, to commission. In conjunction with this work, he has developed a range of contemporary garden ornaments as limited editions. This bird table and weathervane (4.6m high x 75cm in diameter; £1,450) is part of the range, which includes sundials, pot stands and bird baths. Simon works in Cotswold stone, brass copper and stainless steel. Finishes combine painted galvanized steel, verdigris on copper and gilding. Prices start at £350. Contact *Simon Percival, Sunnymeade, Toadsmoor Rd, Brimscombe, Stroud, Glos. GL5 2UF. Tel.: 01453-731478.*

△ Graham Smith of Dorset Weathervanes has been producing vanes for more than eight years and offers over 400 designs to choose from, as well as a design service. Each one is handmade from high-quality steel, zinc-plated and powder-coated against the elements. The weathervane illustrated costs £110 + p & p, including a tailor-made bracket; prices start from £75. All vanes come flat-packed for easy assembly. For a free brochure, with over 40 designs, contact *Dorset Weathervanes, 284 Bournemouth Rd, Charlton Marshall, Blandford, Dorset DT11 9NG. Tel.: 01258-453374.*

△ Exquisitely crafted with ornate gold-leafed numerals and hands depicting the sun and moon, this Medieval clock, is one of a range of outdoor clocks made by Good Directions. It is available in a variety

of sizes and colours, costs from £490 + VAT and delivery. Other outdoor clocks cost from £198 + VAT and delivery. Good Directions engineer the entire clock and specialize in one-offs. Contact them at *Unit 15 Talisman Business Centre, Duncan Rd, Park Gate, Southampton, Hants. SO31 7GA. Tel.: 01489-577828.*

▷ A stone carver specializing in sundials and carved lettering, Ben Jones makes new forms of dial (as shown) as well as more traditional free-standing (plinth) and wall dials. His versions can show a variety of times: Babylonian, Italian or Ancient hours. They can also indicate the time of year marking birthdays, anniversaries, the solstices and equinoxes or the passing months. Price depends on the materials and complexity of the dial face. 'Sum Si Sol Sit' (36 x 27cm) costs about £350. *Ben Jones, 16 Rosebery Rd, Exeter, Devon EX4 6LT. Tel.: 01392-52815.*

▽ Perfect for the garden or the beach, this windbreaker, made from sailcloth and hardwood, is part of Stone Marketing's Ocean Range. It costs £39.99 + p & p, and is available by mail order from *Stone Marketing Ltd, 4 Ashby's Yard, Medway Wharf Rd, Tonbridge, Kent TN9 1RE. Tel.: 01732-771771.*

△ Ivy trails over a rustic concrete head in Wendy Suffield's Dorset garden. Available from Wendy's shop, The Hambledon Gallery, a treasure-trove of ceramics, furniture, *objets d'art* and gifts, this sculpture costs £49.95 and makes a perfect addition to an established garden. *The Hambledon Gallery, 42-44 Salisbury St, Blandford Forum, Dorset DT11 7PR. Tel.: 01258-452880.* See also **Ceramics.**

◁ This ceramic Salamander wall sculpture is one of a series of individually designed pieces suitable for gardens. Claire Murray's work is influenced by the mythical creatures and grotesque characters portrayed in medieval carvings. Claire also designs and makes unique small water fountains. All her pieces are modelled out of frost-proof clay and measure approximately 30 x 30cm. The sculpture costs £200, but prices vary according to design. Contact *Claire Murray, Tel.: 01926-831091 or 01926-425022.*

◁ A folly with a function, the Garden House has been designed by architect Laurie Bradley for urban gardens, and is both attractive and practical. Each one is custom-designed, tailored to uses as diverse as a playhouse, store, workshop, studio or garage. Made from plywood and seasoned timber, it can be supplied with *trompe l'œil* stonework or with a natural finish, and comes in the Classical or Gothic style. Internal folding seats and table are available. Prices start at £2,000 + VAT and include installation. *The Garden House, The Town House, 24 Coptic St, London WC1A 1NT. Tel.: 0181-674 5258.*

▽ A huge source of fun for your children which, once it has weathered, will look as though it has always been in your garden, this playhouse is strong, durable and needs little maintenance. It is one of a range by Brampton Willows, who specialize in making large woven-willow products, from hooded seats and chairs to arbours and garden fencing. They use their own willow and take on commissions. Playhouses cost from £6,000 + VAT, depending on the specification. Order in writing from *Brampton Willows, Upper Farm, Brampton, Beccles, Suffolk NR34 8EH. Tel.: 01502-575891.*

△ Master thatchers Andrew and David Raffle specialize in recreating thatched garden buildings, from Victorian and Edwardian designs, employing traditional materials and construction techniques. They produce any style of building, including summer houses, love seats, sun parlors, gazebos and thatched towers in wood, brick, stone or glazed, then finished and furnished to meet a client's requirements. They are delivered ready to use, and the thatch can be protected against fire. Prices start at £1,460. *Raffles, Church Farm, Main St, Overseal, Derbs. DE12 6LG. Tel.: 01283-762469.*

△ 'The Little Wheelbarrow of Provence' is an exact replica of the ones made in the 1930s on the farms of Provence. The wheelbarrow is hand-crafted from reclaimed pine, treated with wood preservative, and painted to a worn finish by Carolyn Stephenson in soft shades to order. Its compact size (112.5cm/45in. long x 36cm/14½in. high) make it suitable for small gardens, balconies, patios and conservatories. The price is £135 from *Carolyn Stephenson, 96 Tyneham Rd, London SW11 5XP. Tel.: 0171-585 3536*. See also p. 173.

▽ Park Beekeeping Supplies produce handmade skeps and beehives for beekeeping or as a decorative feature in your garden. Skeps are crafted by hand in the traditional manner, and prices begin at £29.40. The popular WBC hive is made in cedar, and is also available painted white. The price for the hive illustrated is £129.95. For further details, contact *Park Beekeeping Supplies, 17 Blackheath Business Centre, 78b Blackheath Hill, London SE10 8BA. Tel.: 0181-694 9960.*

Avant Garden, *77 Ledbury Rd, London W11 2AG (Tel.: 0171-229 4408)*, stock attractive wrought-iron garden furniture.

Benchmark of Oxford, *128 Church Rd, Wheatley, Oxford OX33 1LU (Tel.: 01865-873868)*, specialize in colonial-style furniture, including a Maharajah's Swing Bed.

Brookgate Designs, *Brookgate Farm Oast, Hurst Green, E. Sussex TN19 7QY (Tel.: 01580-860627)*, include among their designs a handsome iroko chair and co-ordinating footstool.

Capital Garden Products, *Gibbs Reed Barn, Pashley Rd, Ticehurst , E. Sussex TN5 7HE (Tel.: 01580-201092)*, make planters and window boxes in fibreglass and cast- and faux-lead, wire topiary frames, pedestals, fountains and magnificent urns.

David Craig, *Units 10/11 Langley Moor Industrial Estate, Durham DH7 8JE (Tel.: 0191-386 0384)*, produces teak furniture from tables, chairs and benches to loungers and parasols.

Freshfield Lane Brickworks Ltd, *Danehill, Haywards Heath, Sussex RH17 7HH (Tel.: 01825-790350)*, manufacture bricks in the traditional way, and use them to make tables, sundials, benches and planters.

Hedgerow Garden Houses, *Rhewl Fach, Prion, Denbigh, Clwyd LL16 4RT (Tel.: 01745-890493)*, design and make a range of summerhouses and playhouses, which are as cheerful and colourful as a gypsy caravan.

Ironart of Bath, *61 Walcot St, Bath, Avon BA1 5BN (Tel.: 01225-446107)*, recreate classic styles in metal, ranging from benches and chairs to curtain rails and candelabra.

Lloyd Loom Direct, *PO Box 75, Spalding, Lincs. PE12 6NB (Tel.: 01775-725876)*, produce Lloyd Loom sofas, chairs and tables, ideal for furnishing a conservatory.

The Traditional Garden Supply Co., *Unit 12, Hewitts Industrial Estate, Elmbridge Rd, Cranleigh, Surrey GU6 8LW (Tel.: 01483-273 366)*, supply useful garden accessories, such as potting benches and New England garden benches with space for storing boots and other paraphernalia.

The South-West

Furniture
Balmain & Balmain, *The Old Rectory, Sandford Orcas, Sherborne, Dorset DT9 4SB p. 41* • Bridge House Carpentry and Joinery, *Bridge House, Mill Lane, Alhampton, Nr Shepton Mallet, Somerset BA4 6PX p. 30* • Simon Clark Cabinetmaking, *Rodgrove Farm, Wincanton, , Somerset BA9 9QU p. 12* • The Feather Bed Company, *Crosslands House, Ash Thomas, Tiverton, Devon EX16 4NU p. 48* • Illingworth and Partridge, *160 North St, Milborne Port, Sherborne, Dorset DT9 5EW p. 24* • i tre, *Chilcombe, Nr Bridport, Dorset DT6 4PN p. 24* • Longpré Cabinet Makers, *Hatherleigh Farm, Wincanton, Somerset BA9 8AB p. 39* • John Lowday, *Exeham Farm, Exebridge, Dulverton, Somerset TA22 9AY p. 19* • John Makepeace Studio, *Parnham House, Beaminster, Dorset DT8 3NA pp. 12, 14 and 30* • Orchard, *14 Mill Lane, Wimborne, Dorset BH21 1LN p. 34* • David Savage, *Westcombe Lane, Bideford, Devon EX39 3JQ p. 24* • Screen Scene, *The Garden House, Mountstephen, Uffculme, Devon EX15 3BX p. 36* • The Somerset Willow Co., *The Wireworks Estate, Bristol Rd, Bridgwater, Somerset TA6 4AP p. 24*

Ceramics
The Hambledon Gallery, *42-44 Salisbury St, Blandford Forum, Dorset DT11 7PR p. 57* • Haytown Pottery, *Haytown, Holsworthy, Devon EX22 7UW p. 55* • Paul Jackson, *Helland Bridge Pottery, Helland Bridge, Nr Bodmin, Cornwall PL30 4QR p. 61* • Danka Napiorkowska, *Little Treforda, Trewalder, Delabole, Cornwall PL33 9EY p. 68* • Piggery Pottery, *Grange Barn, Grange Rd, Wareham, Dorset BH20 5AL p. 54* • Yerja Ceramics & Textiles, *Mill Rise, Ford Rd, Bampton, Devon EX16 9LW p. 51*

Glass
Martin Donlin, *Tel.: 01202-739063 p. 78* • Shakspeare Glassworks, *Riverside Pl., Taunton, Somerset TA1 1JJ p. 78*

Silver
Caroline Lytton, *Tel.: 01643-705797 p. 83*

Textiles
Callan & Horsey, *Stone House, Frenchmill Lane, Shaftesbury, Dorset SP7 0LT p. 9* • Helyne Jennings, *Pennyford Cottage, Burrington, Umberleigh, Devon EX37 9LN p. 98* • Miller & Shültz, *South Kenwood, Kenton, Exeter, Devon EX6 8EX p. 91*

Mirrors
Art History, *The Stables Studios, Nethercott Barton, Iddesleigh, Nr Winkleigh, Devon EX19 8SN p. 104* • William Austin, *38 Middle Leigh, Street, Somerset BA16 0LH p. 102*

Decorative Accessories
P.H. Coate & Son, *Meare Green Court, Stoke St. Gregory, Taunton, Somerset TA3 6HY p. 120* • Veronica Mills, *Paradise House, 1 Queen's Sq., Cullompton, Devon EX15 1DB p. 124*

Kitchen Accessories and Tableware
P.H. Coate & Son, *Meare Green Court, Stoke St. Gregory, Taunton, Somerset TA3 6HY p. 129* • Stephen Coe, *10 Beaufoy Close, The Sycamores, Shaftesbury, Dorset SP7 8PT p. 126* • Orchard, *14 Mill Lane, Wimborne, Dorset BH21 1LN p. 127* • Robinson and Cornish, *Southay House, Oakwood Close, Roundswell, Barnstaple, Devon EX31 3NJ p. 127* • Somerset Creative Products, *Charlecote, Mark, Somerset TA9 4PX p. 127*

Crafts for Children
The Children's Room, *North St, Langport, Somerset TA10 9RH p. 135*

Decorative Fixtures
Clayton Munroe Ltd, *Kingston, Staverton, Totnes, Devon TQ9 6AR p. 160* • Turnstyle Designs, *1 Bridge Chambers, The Square, Barnstaple, Devon EX31 1HB p. 161*

Wall Coverings
The English Stamp Company, *Sunnydown, Worth Matravers, Dorset BH19 3JP p. 167*

The Garden
Paul Anderson, *104 West St, Hartland, Devon EX39 6BQ p. 174* • Crafted Comfort Furniture Design, *Tredrossel House, Sheviock, Nr Torpoint, Cornwall PL11 3DZ p. 178* • Dorset Weathervanes, *284 Bournemouth Rd, Charlton Marshall, Blandford, Dorset DT11 9NG p. 181* • Cara Frost, *Claycastle Cottage, South Perrot, Beaminster, Dorset DT8 3HU p.174* • The Hambledon Gallery, *42-44 Salisbury St, Blandford Forum, Dorset DT11 7PR p. 182* • Hare Lane Pottery, *Cranborne, Wimborne, Dorset BH21 5QT p. 170* • Ben Jones, *16 Rosebery Rd, Exeter, Devon EX4 6LT p. 182* • Somerset Creative Products, *Charlecote, Mark, Somerset TA9 4PX p. 179*

South and SE England

Furniture
Artifex, *3 Vale Rd, Tunbridge Wells, Kent TN1 1BS; and 258 Royal Victoria Pl., Upper Mall, Tunbridge Wells, Kent TN1 2SS p. 27* • George Clark, *The High St, Stockbridge, Hants. SO20 6HF p. 33* • Julian Coode, *Nailbourne Forge, Littlebourne, Canterbury, Kent CT3 1TX p. 33* • Brendan J. Devitt-Spooner, *Wood Design Workshops, The Acre, Dappers Lane, Angmering, W. Sussex BN16 4EN p. 24* • Annie Eadie, *The Heveningham Collection, Peacock Cottage, Church Hill, Nether Wallop, Hants. SO20 8EY p. 18* • Mark Francis, *New Street House, New St, Petworth, W. Sussex GU28 0AS p. 22* • Harriet Ann Beds, *Standen Farm, Smarden Rd, Biddenden, Nr Ashford, Kent TN27 8JT p. 45* • Bill Gill, *13 Riverbank, East Molesey, Surrey KT8 9BH p. 19* • The Iron Bed Company, *Southfield Park, Delling Lane, Old Bosham, W. Sussex PO18 8NN p. 46* • Stephen Owen, *Whipley Studio, Whipley Manor Farm, Bramley, Surrey GU5 0LL p. 44* • Sparewood, *Cambridge Cottage, Cambridge Lane, Lynsted, Kent ME9 9JB p. 12*

Ceramics
Sylph Baier, *Tin Star Studio, 38 Cheltenham Pl., Brighton, E. Sussex BN1 4AB p. 53* • Cartwright Ceramics, *Blue Cat House Studios, 10a & 11 Howard Rd, Brighton, E. Sussex BN2 2TP p. 58* • Kenneth Clark Ceramics, *The North Wing, Southover Grange, Southover Rd, Lewes, E. Sussex BN17 1TP p. 66* • Emma Falcke, *Studio One, 1 Victoria St, Rochester, Kent ME1 1XJ p. 60* • Jane Healey, *32 Down Park Cottages, West Harting, Nr Petersfield, Hants. GU31 5PF p. 50* • Genevieve Neilson, *The Gallery, 13 Victoria St, Englefield Green, Surrey TW20 0QY p. 65* • Anthony Parfitt, *6 Springvale North, Dartford, Kent DA1 2LL p. 63*

Glass
Lisa Cross, *81a Filsham Road, St Leonard's-on-Sea, E. Sussex TN38 0PE p. 76* • Glassworks, *39 Trafalgar St, Brighton, E. Sussex BN1 4ED p. 72* • David Weeks, *The Glassblowers Workshop, The Star Brewery, Castle Ditch Lane, Lewes, E. Sussex BN7 1YJ p. 74* • Heidi Westgate, *Unit 3a, The Star Brewery, Castle Ditch Lane, Lewes, E. Sussex BN7 1YJ p. 70*

Silver
Anton Pruden & Rebecca Smith, *Turner Dumbrell Workshops, North End, Ditchling, E. Sussex BN6 8TD p. 84* • Richardson & Ottewill, *Evegate, Station Rd, Smeeth, Ashford, Kent TN26 6SX p. 81*

Textiles
Neil Bottle, *Tel.: 01843-592953 p. 98* • The Language of Flowers, *30 The Pantiles, Royal Tunbridge Wells, Kent TN2 5TN p. 91*

Mirrors
Belvedere, *Unit 3, Hartley Business Park, Selborne, Alton, Hants. GU34 3HS p. 107* • Alex Jones, *Elms Lodge, Elms House, Twyford, Hants. SO21 1QF p. 106*

Decorative Accessories
Coldpiece Pottery, *Hound Green, Hook, Hants. RG27 8LQ p. 115* • Maggie Philo, *18 Walpole Rd, Kemp Town, Brighton, E. Sussex BN2 2EA p. 124* • Porta Romana, *Lower Froyle, Alton, Hants. GU34 4LS p. 116* • Ribbons & Bows, *19 East St, Petworth, W. Sussex GU28 0AB p. 123* • Val Roet, *29 Upper Pk Rd, Kingston, Surrey KT2 5LB p. 124* • Touch Design Ltd, *PO Box 60, Andover, Hants. SP11 6SS p. 122*

Kitchen Accessories and Tableware
Lois Carr, *Quedley Copse, Flimwell, Wadhurst, E. Sussex TN5 7NY p. 130* • Hermitage Furniture, *The Hermitage, Castle Rd, Sandgate, Kent CT20 3 AG p. 127* • Touch Design Ltd, *PO Box 60, Andover, Hants. SP11 6SS p. 131*

Crafts for Children
Stevenson Brothers, *The Workshop, Ashford Rd, Bethersden, Ashford, Kent TN26 3AP p. 133*

Flooring
Stonell Ltd, *Unit 1, Bockingfold, Ladham Rd, Goudhurst, Kent TN17 1LY p. 143* • Tintawn Weaving Co., *The Old Kings Head Court, 11 High St, Dorking, Surrey RH4 1AR p. 145*

Lighting
Euan Cunningham, *Treve Cottage, River Common, Petworth, W. Sussex GU28 9BH p. 151*

Decorative Fixtures
James Cox, *Tin Star Studio, 38 Cheltenham Pl., Brighton, E. Sussex BN1 4AB p. 162*

The Garden
Black Forge Art, *Owley Farm, Wittersham, Isle of Oxney, Kent T N30 7HJ p. 180* • Brookgate Designs, *Brookgate Farm Oast, Hurst Green, E. Sussex TN19 7QY p. 184* • Sarah Burgoyne Revivals, *Whyly, East Hoathly, E. Sussex BN8 6EL p. 176* • Capital Garden Products, *Gibbs Reed Barn, Pashley Rd, Ticehurst, E. Sussex TN5 7HE p. 184* • Mark Francis, *New Street House, New St, Petworth, W. Sussex GU28 0AS p.173* • Freshfield Lane Brickworks Ltd, *Danehill, Haywards Heath, W. Sussex RH17 7HH p. 184* • Frolics of Winchester, *82 Canon St, Winchester, Hants. SO23 9JQ p. 171* • Gaze Burvill, *Plain Farm, Old Dairy, East Tisted, Hants. GU34 3RT p. 175* • Good Directions, *Unit 15 Talisman Business Centre, Duncan Rd, Park Gate, Southampton, Hants. SO31 7GA p. 181* • Kemptown Terracotta, *5 Arundel Rd, Brighton, E. Sussex BN2 5TE p. 170* • Stone Marketing Ltd, *4 Ashby's Yard, Medway Wharf Rd, Tonbridge, Kent TN9 1RE p. 182* • Sussex Trugs Ltd, *Thomas Smith's Trug Shop, Hailsham Rd, Herstmonceux, E. Sussex BN27 4LH p. 179* • The Traditional Garden Supply Co., *Unit 12, Hewitts Industrial Estate, Elmbridge Rd, Cranleigh, Surrey GL6 8LW p. 184*

London

Furniture
The Barn, *238 St. Paul's Rd, London N1 2LJ p. 46* • Beaumont & Fletcher, *98 Waterford Rd, London SW6 2HA p. 41* • Rupert Bevan, *40 Fulham High St, London SW6 3LQ p. 42* • Ben Brooks, *1-4 Prince of Wales Terr., London W4 2EY p. 22* • Codrington Furniture, *Tel.: 0171-498 9960 p. 30* • Cara Crawley, *228 Hammersmith Grove, London W6 7HG p. 36* • CVP Designs, *27 Bruton Pl., London W1X 7AB p. 14* • Tom Faulkner Designs, *13 Petley Rd, London W6 9SU p. 16* • Grand Illusions, *2-4 Crown Rd, St Margaret's, Twickenham, Middx TW1 3EE p. 26* • The Hand Made Tallboy Company, *16 Brookland Rise, London NW11*

Grey Trellises, *Broadhinton Yard, 77a North St, London SW4 0HQ p. 172* • Lucy Fielden, *Tel.: 0171-259 5108 p. 173* • The Garden House, *The Town House, 24 Coptic St, London WC1A 1NT p. 183* • Indian Ocean Trading Company, *28 Ravenswood Rd, London SW12 9PJ p. 177* • Duncan H. McLaren Ltd, *10 St. James's Pl., London SW1A 1NP p. 175* • Park Beekeeping Supplies, *17 Blackheath Business Centre, 78b Blackheath Hill, London SE10 8BA p. 184* • Carolyn Stephenson, *96 Tyneham Rd, London SW11 5XP pp. 173 and 184.*

South Central England

Furniture
Acres Farm, *Bradfield, Reading, Berks. RG7 6JH p. 34* • Cato Furniture Makers, *The Epstein Building, Cato St, Bristol BS5 6JL p. 24* • Jim Crockatt, *Pococks Cottage, Mariners Lane, Bradfield, Berks. RG7 6HX pp. 13 and 29* • The Felbrigg Design Company, *The Coach House, 4 Park Lane, Sutton Benger, Wilts. SN15 4RN p. 35* • Lucinda Leech Furniture, *King St, Jericho, Oxford OX2 6DF p. 21* • Trevor Moore Handmade Furniture Ltd, *The Wharf Centre, Couch Lane, Devizes, Wilts. SN10 1EB p. 15* • Trannon Furniture Ltd, *Chilhampton Farm, Wilton, Salisbury, Wilts. SP2 0AB p. 24*

Ceramics
Julie Arnall, *26 Woodwaye, Watford, Herts. WD1 4NW p. 66* • Bowled Over, *Manor Farmhouse, Patney, Nr Devizes, Wilts. SN10 3RB p. 61* • Clays Handmade Tiles, *110 Leavesden Rd, Watford, Herts. WD2 5EG p. 67* • Fired Earth, *Twyford Mill, Oxford Rd, Adderbury, Oxon OX17 3HP p. 67* • Jo Firth, *Dorncliffe, Burden's Heath, Upper Bucklebury, Reading, Berks. RG7 6SX p. 56* • John Jelfs, *Cotswold Pottery, Clapton Row, Bourton-on-the- Water, Glos. GL54 2DN p. 62* • Love Unlimited Ceramics, *39 South St, Bedminster, Bristol BS3 3AU p. 61* • Joanna Still, *4 Beckford Cottages, Hindon, Salisbury, Wilts. SP3 6ED p. 50*

Glass
Ruth Dresman Glass, *The Meads, West Knoyle, Warminster, Wilts. BA12 6AE p. 78* • Gerald Paxton, Glass Heritage Ltd, *Reynolds Warehouse, The Docks, Glos. GL1 2EN p. 73* • Gaynor Ringland, *2 The Grove, Portway, Warminster, Wilts. BA12 8QL p. 73*

Silver
Boursot, *Tel.: 01488-668628/Fax: 01488-668853 p. 81* • Patricia Hamilton, *The Mill, Hardwick, Witney, Oxon OX8 7QE p. 80*

Textiles
Early's of Witney, *Witney Mill, Witney, Oxon OX8 5EB p. 95* • Fired Earth, *Twyford Mill, Oxford Rd, Adderbury, Oxon OX17 3HP p. 98* • Liz Lippiatt, *The Textile Workshop, 7 Brewery Arts, Brewery Ct, Cirencester, Glos. GL7 1JH p. 100*

Mirrors
Susan Nelson, *Folly Bridge Workshops, Thames St, Oxford OX1 1SU p. 105* • Tors Decorative Artist, *Bears, Shepherds Green, Henley-on- Thames, Oxon RG9 4QR p. 104*

Clocks
Appalachia, *14a George St, St. Albans, Herts. AL3 4ER p. 112* • Handmade in Wiltshire, *Sandiacres, Etchilhampton, Devizes, Wilts. SN10 3JP p. 111* • Donald Yule Clocks, *23a Trowbridge Rd, Bradford-on-Avon, Wilts. BA15 1EE p. 111*

Decorative Accessories
Acres Farm, *Bradfield, Reading, Berks. RG7 6JH p. 117* • Allia Design, *The Black Cabin Barn, Hailes, Cheltenham, Glos. GL54 5PB p. 121* • Amanda Baird, *Barford Cliff Cottage, Downton, Salisbury, Wilts. SP5 3QF p. 119* • Jane Gordon-Smith, *Yew Glen House, Castle St. Mere, Wilts. BA12 6JE p. 123* • Katie Potter, *The*

Granary Studio, *Palmersmoor House, Iver, Bucks. SL0 9LG p. 122* • Timothy Richards Architectural Fine Art Commissions, *59 West View Rd, Keynsham, Bristol BS18 1BQ p. 121*

Kitchen Accessories and Tableware
Robert Smith, *1 Homeleigh, Whempstead, Ware, Herts. SG12 0PL p. 131* • Swanalong, *Middle Farm, Taston, Charlbury, Oxford OX7 3JL p. 130*

Crafts for Children
Adams & Co., *Kingston Rd, Bradford-on-Avon, Wilts. BA15 1BD p. 137* • Jim Crockatt, *Pococks Cottage, Mariners Lane, Bradfield, Berks, RG7 6HX p. 134* • Sarah-Jane Muir Upholstery, *Angel Farm, Monks Alley, Binfield, Berks. RG12 5PA p. 138*

Flooring
A.R.T. Hardwood Flooring, *7 Deans Close, Amersham, Bucks. HP6 6LW p. 141* • Fired Earth, *Twyford Mill, Oxford Rd, Adderbury, Oxon OX17 3HP pp. 143, 144 and 146*

Lighting
The Light Brigade, *28 Rodney Rd, Cheltenham, Glos. GL50 1JJ p. 151* • Strawberry Crafts Co-operative, *Beckford Stores, Beckford, Nr Tewkesbury, Glos. GL20 7AD p. 152* • Robert Welch Studio Shop, *Lower High St, Chipping Campden, , Glos. GL55 6OY p. 148* • Jack Wimperis, *Piccadilly Mill, Lower St, Stroud, Glos. GL5 2HT p. 153*

Decorative Fixtures
Julie Arnall, *26 Woodwaye, Watford, Herts. WD1 4NW p. 161* • The Felbrigg Design Company, *The Coach House, 4 Park Lane, Sutton Benger, Wilts. SN15 4RN p. 159* • Hang-Ups Accessories Ltd, *Unit 7, Lyncroft Farm Workshops, Perrotts Brook, Cirencester, Glos. GL7 7BW p. 159* • Resina Designs, *Unit 6a, Burnett Industrial Estate, Wrington, Bristol BS18 7QU p. 160*

Wall Coverings
Alexander Beauchamp, *Vulcan House, Stratton Rd, Glos. GL1 4HL p. 164* • Fired Earth, *Twyford Mill, Oxford Rd, Adderbury, Oxon OX17 3HP p. 164*

The Garden
Benchmark of Oxford, *128 Church Rd, Wheatley, Oxford OX33 1LU p. 184* • Silas Birtwistle and Leo Zinovieff, *The Stableyard, Coleshill, Nr Faringdon, Oxon SN7 7NB p. 174* • The Garden Ropework Company, *47 West Hill, Hitchin, Herts. SG5 2HY p. 170* • HMP Ltd, *Ditchford Farm, Moreton-in-Marsh, Glos. GL56 9RD p. 172* • Ironart of Bath, *61 Walcot St, Bath, Avon BA1 5BN p. 184* • Jane Hogben Ceramics, *Grove House, East Common, Gerrards Cross, Bucks. SL9 7AF p. 170* • Landscape Ornament Company Ltd, *Long Barn, Patney, Devizes, Wilts. SN10 3RB p. 171* • Leisuredeck Ltd, *Maylands House, Maylands Ave., Hemel Hempstead, Herts. HP2 7DE p. 172* • Simon Percival, *Sunnymeade, Toadsmoor Rd, Brimscombe, Stroud, Glos. GL5 2UF p. 181* • Rusco Marketing, *Little Faringdon Mill, Lechlade, Glos. GL7 3QQ p. 176* • Terrace & Garden Ltd, *Orchard House, Patmore End, Ugley, Bishop's Stortford, Herts. CM22 6JA p. 181*

East Anglia

Furniture
Alouette Innovation Ltd, *PO Box 2264, Epping, Essex CM16 4AH p. 24* • Bed Bazaar, *The Old Station Building, Station Rd, Framlingham, Suffolk IP13 9EE p. 48* • Glenn Hinton Furniture, *Croft Rd, Sudbury, Suffolk CO10 6RD p. 20* • Lovelace, *Broad Piece, Soham, Cambridge CB7 5EL p. 30* • Toby Winteringham, *Whitehouse, Bawsey, King's Lynn, Norfolk PE32 1EY p. 44*

Ceramics
Hazle Ceramics, *Stallions Yard, Codham Hall, Great*

Warley, *Brentwood, Essex CM13 3JT p. 65* • Sally Reilly, *Lyndhurst Studios, 92 Station Rd, Soham, Ely, Cambs. CB7 5DZ p. 54*

Textiles
Old Town, *32 Elm Hill, Norwich NR3 1HG p. 90*

Decorative Accessories
Amanda Leschallas, *M.C. Arts, Moatwood Cottage, Gifford's Lane, Wickhambrook, Newmarket, Suffolk CB8 8PQ p. 120* • Anna Nockolds, *The Old Laundry, Unit 3, Church Hill, Starston, Harleston, Norfolk IP20 9PF p. 122*

Kitchen Accessories and Tableware
Anna Nockolds, *The Old Laundry, Unit 3, Church Hill, Starston, Harleston, Norfolk IP20 9PF p. 129*

Crafts for Children
Haddon Ltd, *5 Telford Rd, Clacton-on-Sea, Essex CO15 4LP p. 134*

Flooring
Waveney Apple Growers Ltd, *Common Rd, Aldeby, Suffolk NR34 0BL p. 145*

Lighting
Hugh St. Clair Designs, *5 Fish Hill, Holt, Norfolk NR25 6BD p. 153*

Decorative Fixtures
The Bradley Collection, *The Granary, Flowton Brook, Flowton, Suffolk IP8 4LJ p. 156* • Cambridge Home Fashions, *Unit 36, Dry Drayton Industries, Scotland Rd, Dry Drayton, Cambridge CB3 8AT p. 158*

Wall Coverings
First Class Stamps Ltd, *Hall Staithe, Fakenham, Norfolk NR21 9BW p. 166*

The Garden
Brampton Willows, *Upper Farm, Brampton, Beccles, Suffolk NR34 8EH p. 183* • The Bulbeck Foundry, *Reach Rd, Burwell, Cambs. CB5 0AH p. 171* • Bulmer Brick & Tile Co. Ltd, *The Brickfields, Bulmer, Nr Sudbury, Suffolk CO10 7EF p. 169*

The Midlands

Furniture
Ben Casson, *Wobage Farm, Upton Bishop, Nr Ross-on-Wye, Hereford HR9 7QP p. 28* • Robin Clarke Furniture, *Keeper's House, Brockmanton, Pudleston, Nr Leominster, Hereford HR6 0QU p. 24* • Derwent Upholstery, *Greenhill Industrial Estate, Greenhill Lane, Riddings, Derbs. DE55 4BR p. 41* • Essential Items, *Church House, Plungar, Nottingham NG13 0JA p. 42* • Philip Hearsey, *Monkhall Court, Callow, Hereford HR2 8DA p. 15* • Hoppé Design, *The Bell House, Kingsland, Leominster, Hereford HR6 9RU pp. 26 and 48* • Roger Oates Design Associates, *The Long Barn, Eastnor, Ledbury, Hereford HR8 1EL p. 40* • Amanda Pearce, *74 Carlingford Rd, Hucknall, Notts. NG15 7AG p. 36* • Recollections Furniture Company, *Whitehill Park, Weobley, Hereford HR4 8QE p. 18* • Adrian Reynolds, *Tel./Fax: 01952-433222 p. 47* • Paul Shepherd, *Lower Nicholson, Docklow, Leominster, Hereford HR6 0SL p. 16* • Lee Sinclair Furniture, *Endon House, Laneham, Nr Retford, Notts. DN22 0NA p. 23* • Andrew Varah, *Little Walton, Nr Pailton, Rugby, Warwickshire CV23 0QL p. 13* • Neil Wyn Jones, *Artizana, The Village, Prestbury, Cheshire SK10 4DG pp. 14 and 33*

Ceramics
Karen Atherley, *4 Tower Court, Thorney, Peterborough PE6 0PW p. 51* • Country Matters, *Unit 1, Albert Mill, Compstall, Stockport, Cheshire SK6 5HN p. 65* • De La Torre Tiles, *The Courtyard, The Old Rectory, Stoke Lacy, Hereford HR7 4HH p. 67* • Wendy Johnson, *Tel.: 0115-960 7940 p. 50* • Suzanne Katkhuda, *Tel.: 01604-*

880800/Fax: 01604-880884 *p. 60* • Penkridge Ceramics, *Argent Works, Bott Lane, Walsall, W. Mids WS1 2JJ p. 63* Jane Temple Lamps & China, *Reaside Farm, Neen Savage, Cleobury Mortimer, Kidderminster, Worcs. DY14 8ES p. 65* • Whichford Pottery, *Whichford, Nr Shipston-on-Stour, Warwickshire CF36 5 PG p. 66*

Glass

Blowzone Glass Studio, *Platts Rd, Amblecote, Stourbridge, W. Midlands DY8 4YR p. 76* • Greenhalgh Glass, *The Glassblowing Workshop, Caudwell's Mill, Derbs. DE4 2EB p. 76* • Hothouse, *7 Lumsdale Mill, Lower Lumsdale, Matlock, Derbs. D4 5EX p. 74*

Silver

Kevin O'Dwyer, *Artizana, The Village, Prestbury, Cheshire SK10 4DG p. 82* • Keith Tyssen, *80 Gell St, Sheffield S3 7QW p. 85*

Textiles

Antique Designs, *4 Stretton Hall Mews, Hall Lane, Lower Stretton, Cheshire WA4 4NY p. 90* • Alison Dupernex, *19 Britannia Sq., Worcester WR1 3DG p. 91* • Niki Tyson, *4 Waterloo Cottages, Compstall Rd, Romiley, Stockport, Cheshire SK6 4JE p. 100*

Mirrors

Lynn Hodgson, *Wobage Workshops, Upton Bishop, Ross-on- Wye, Hereford HR9 7QP p. 105* • Claudia Petley, *Lower Nicholson, Docklow, Leominster, Hereford HR6 0SL p. 104*

Clocks

Fio Design Associates, *1302 Custard Factory, Gibb St, Digbeth, Birmingham B9 4AA p. 110* • Tic Tok Design, *162 Barrow Rd, Sileby, Loughborough, Leics. LE12 7LR p. 109*

Decorative Accessories

The Glanarrow Box Company, *Glanarrow Mill, Eardisland, Hereford HR6 9BY p. 119* • Amanda Pearce, *74 Carlingford Rd, Hucknall, Notts. NG15 7AG p. 117*

Flooring

Alan Foulds, *Orchard Cottage, Buskwood, Hope-under-Dinmore, Hereford HR6 0PX p. 146* • Roger Oates Designs, *The Long Barn, Eastnor, Ledbury, Hereford HR8 1EL p. 143*

Lighting

Eryka Isaak, *12 Lickey Coppice, Cofton Hackett, Birmingham B45 8PG p. 150* • Unit 9, Shed Eleven Studio, *12 Plumptre St, The Lace Market, Nottingham NG1 1JL p. 150* • Robert Welch Studio Shop, *19 Old Sq., Warwick CV34 4RU p. 148*

Decorative Fixtures

Harrison Drape, *Bradford St, Birmingham B12 0PE p. 157* • Joseph Tipper Ltd, *Century Works, Moat St, Willenhall, W. Midlands WV13 1FZ p. 161*

Wall Coverings

Eleanor Allitt, *Thickthorn Cottage, 108 Leamington Rd, Kenilworth, Warwickshire CV8 2AA p. 166* • The Painted Finish, *Unit 6B, Hatton Country World, Hatton, Warwick CV35 8XA p. 167*

The Garden

L'Art du Bois Ltd, *Uphampton House, Shobdon, Nr Leominster, Hereford HR6 9PA p. 178* • Kettler (GB) Ltd, *Kettler House, Merse Rd, North Moons Moat, Redditch, Worcs. B98 9HL p.173* • Claire Murray, *Tel.: 01926-831091/425022 p. 182* • Raffles, *Church Farm, Main St, Overseal, Derbs. DE12 6LG p. 183* • Steamer Furniture, *The Forge, Wigmore, Leominster, Hereford HR6 9UA p. 179* • Whichford Pottery, *Whichford, Nr Shipston-on-Stour, Warwickshire CV36 5PG p. 169*

Wales

Furniture

Mark Rowan Furniture, *Garreg Fawr, Porthyrhyd, Llanwrda, Dyfed SA19 8NY p. 30*

Ceramics

Wilma Allan, *Craig Ddu, Llanthony, Abergavenny, Gwent NP7 7NW p. 52* • Morgen Hall, *Studio 5, Chapter Arts Centre, Market Rd, Canton, Cardiff CF5 1QE p. 59*

Glass

Georgina Lester, *The Workhouse, Hatherleigh Pl., Union Rd, Abergavenny, Gwent NP7 9SA p. 74*

Textiles

Melin Tregwynt, *Tregwynt Mill, Castle Morris, Haverfordwest, Pembrokeshire SA62 5UX p. 96* • Alison Morton, *Eagles Yard, Machynlleth, Powys SY20 8AG p. 94*

Decorative Accessories

Young Jones, *'Wooden World', Bryn St, Newtown, Powys SY16 2HW p. 119*

Kitchen Accessories and Tableware

Occasional Art, *176 Ffordd-y-Parc, Litchard, Bridgend, Mid Glam. CF31 1RA p. 131*

Crafts for Children

Jigsaw, *Llanfairynghornwy, Gwynedd LL65 4LW p. 135* • Barry Skinner, *Turnpike Cottage, Traeth, Beddgelert, Gwynedd LL55 4YF p. 137*

The Garden

Hedgerow Garden Houses, *Rhewl Fach, Prion, Denbigh, Clwyd LL16 4RT p. 184*

Northern England

Furniture

A'Fos, *Lake Rd, Bowness-on-Windermere, Cumbria LA23 2JJ p. 21* • Steve Allen Cabinet Makers, *Hollin Bridge Mill, Hollin Bridge St, Blackburn, Lancs. BB2 4BB p. 30* • Duncan Copley Contemporary Furniture Design, *The Old Co-op Yard, Clarence St, Ulverston, Cumbria LA12 7JJ pp. 27, 31 and 42* • David Crews & Co., *Church House, Ebberston, Scarborough, N. Yorks. YO13 9NR p. 26* • The Iron Design Company, *Summer Carr Farm, Thornton-Le- Moor, Northallerton, N. Yorks. DL6 3SG p. 16*

Ceramics

Jessica Ball, *12 River St, Haworth, W. Yorks. BD22 8ND p. 50* • Sophie Hamilton, *Deerholme Pottery, High Marishes, Malton, N. Yorks. YO17 0UQ p. 61* • Porcellana, *63 Station Parade, Harrogate, N. Yorks. HG1 1ST p. 54*

Glass

Jane Charles Studio Glass, *Units 19 and 20 Premier Workshops, Whitehouse Rd, Scotswood, Newcastle upon Tyne NE15 6EP p. 72* • Mark Prest Glass, *Manchester Craft Centre, 17 Oak St, Manchester M4 5JB p. 78*

Silver

Philippa Merriman, *Westfield House, West Rd, Lancaster LA1 5PE p. 84* • Frances Julie Whitelaw, *Cleveland Crafts Centre, 57 Gilkes St, Middlesbrough, Cleveland TS1 5EL p. 84*

Textiles

Katherine Fisher, *369 Holcombe Rd, Greenmount, Bury, Lancs. BL8 4DT p. 99*

Mirrors

Adam Jackson, *Poplars Farm, Beningbrough, York YO6 1BY p. 106*

Clocks

Louise Byrne, *28 Firwood Ave., Urmston, Manchester M41 9PJ p. 111* • The Cardboard Clock Company, *14 East St, Newton Hill, Wakefield, W. Yorks. WF1 2PY p. 109* • ZeD Clock Company, *23 New Mount St, Manchester M4 4DE p. 113*

Decorative Accessories

Yellow House, *Pyes Mill, Station Rd, Bentham, Lancaster LA2 7LJ p. 116*

Crafts for Children

Bundles Design Ltd, *222 Century Building, Brunswick Dock, Liverpool L3 4BJ p. 138* • Poppy Ltd, *44 High St, Yarm, Cleveland TS15 9AE p. 138*

Flooring

Happy Mats Ltd, *Fair Rigg Cottage, Newby Bridge, Ulverston, Cumbria LA12 8NQ p. 145* • Paris Ceramics, *4 Montpellier St, Harrogate, N. Yorks. HG1 2RY p. 142*

Lighting

Definitive, *37 Catharine St, Liverpool L8 7NE p. 151* • The Protector Lamp & Lighting Co., *Lansdowne Rd, Eccles, Manchester M30 9PH p. 152*

Wall Coverings

Angela Beaumont, *12-14 Hainworth Village, Keighley, W. Yorks. BD21 5QH p. 165* • The Stencil Library, *Stocksfield Hall, Stocksfield, Northumb. NE43 7TN p. 166*

The Garden

Cobblestone Designs, *Hilltop, Wennington, Lancaster LA2 8NY p. 172* • David Craig, *Units: 10/11, Langley Moor Industrial Estate, Durham DH7 8JE p. 184* • Lloyd Loom Direct, *PO Box 75, Spalding, Lincs. PE12 6NB p. 184* • Keith Mott, *2 Chapel Row, Aldfield, Ripon, N. Yorks. HG4 3BG p. 179*

Scotland

Furniture

Clock House Furniture, *The Old Stables, Overhailes, Haddington, E. Lothian EH41 3SB p. 42*

Ceramics

John O'Groats Pottery, *Unit 3, John O'Groats, Caithness KW1 4YR p. 63*

Glass

Deborah Fladgate, *Fladgate Glass Studio, Greenside House, Leslie, Fife KY6 3DF p. 72* • Sue Keelan Glass, *The Stables, Cargill, Perth PH2 6DS p. 70* • Katrina Walker-Hamlett, *Sesame and Lillies, The Tower, Woodhill, Kinellar, Aberdeen AB2 0RZ p. 76*

Silver

Malcolm Appleby, *Crathes Station, Banchory, Kincardineshire AB3 3JE p. 87*

Textiles

Ousdale Weaving Ltd, *Ousdale, Berriedale, Caithness KW7 6HD p. 96* • Tait & Style, *Brae Studio, Old Academy, Back Rd, Stromness, Orkney KW16 3AW p. 94*

Mirrors

The Lansdowne Collection, *35 Lansdowne Cres., Glasgow G20 6NH p. 103*

Clocks

Anne Finlay, *7 Bellevue Terr., Edinburgh EH7 4DT p. 109*

Crafts for Children

Camno Workshop, *Railway Cottage, Camno Crossing, by Newtyle, Angus PH12 8SW p. 136* • Alan and Catherine Lees, *38 Patna Rd, Kirkmichael, Ayrshire KA19 7PJ p. 134*

Wall Coverings

The Lansdowne Collection, *35 Lansdowne Cres., Glasgow G20 6NH p. 166*

INDEX